Land Warfare: Brassey's New Battlefield
Weapons Systems and Technology Series

Volume 6

MILITARY
HELICOPTERS

Land Warfare:
Brassey's New Battlefield Weapons Systems and Technology Series

Executive Editor: Colonel R G Lee OBE, Former Military Director of Studies, Royal Military College of Science, Shrivenham, UK

Editor-in-Chief: Professor Frank Hartley, Vice Chancellor, Cranfield Institute of Technology

The success of the first series on Battlefield Weapons Systems and Technology and the pace of advances in military technology has prompted Brassey's to produce a new Land Warfare series. This series updates subjects covered in the original series and also covers completely new areas. The books are written for military men who wish to advance their professional knowledge. In addition, they are intended to aid anyone who is interested in the design, development and production of military equipment.

Volume 1 Guided Weapons – R G Lee *et al*

Volume 2 Explosives, Propellants and Pyrotechnics – A Bailey and S G Murray

Volume 3 Noise in the Military Environment – R F Powell and M R Forrest

Volume 4 Ammunition – P R Courtney-Green and E G Archer

Volume 5 Communications and Information Systems for Battlefield Command and Control – A J Sammes and M A Rice

Volume 6 Military Helicopters – E J Everett-Heath *et al*

For full details of titles in the series, please contact your local Brassey's/Pergamon office.

MILITARY HELICOPTERS

E. J. EVERETT-HEATH, G. M. MOSS,
A. W. MOWAT and K. E. REID
Royal Military College of Science, Shrivenham, UK

BRASSEY'S (UK)
(Member of the Maxwell Pergamon Publishing Corporation)

LONDON · OXFORD · WASHINGTON · NEW YORK · BEIJING
FRANKFURT · SÃO PAULO · SYDNEY · TOKYO · TORONTO

UK (Editorial)	Brassey's (UK) Ltd., 24 Gray's Inn Road, London WC1X 8HR, England
(Orders, all except North America)	Brassey's (UK) Ltd., Headington Hill Hall, Oxford OX3 0BW, England
USA (Editorial)	Brassey's (US) Inc., 8000 Westpark Drive, Fourth Floor, McLean, Virginia 22102, USA
(Orders, North America)	Brassey's (US) Inc., Front and Brown Streets, Riverside, New Jersey 08075, USA Tel (toll free): 800 257 5755
PEOPLE'S REPUBLIC OF CHINA	Pergamon Press, Room 4037, Qianmen Hotel, Beijing, People's Republic of China
FEDERAL REPUBLIC OF GERMANY	Pergamon Press GmbH, Hammerweg 6, D-6242 Kronberg, Federal Republic of Germany
BRAZIL	Pergamon Editora Ltda, Rua Eça de Queiros, 346, CEP 04011, Paraiso, São Paulo, Brazil
AUSTRALIA	Brassey's Australia Pty Ltd., PO Box 544, Potts Point, NSW 2011, Australia
JAPAN	Pergamon Press, 5th Floor, Matsuoka Central Building, 1-7-1 Nishishinjuku, Shinjuku-ku, Tokyo 160, Japan
CANADA	Pergamon Press Canada Ltd., Suite No. 271, 253 College Street, Toronto, Ontario, Canada M5T 1R5

Copyright © 1990 Brassey's (UK) Ltd.

First edition 1990

Library of Congress Cataloging in Publication Data
Military helicopters/E. J. Everett-Heath . . . [et al.]. — 1st ed.
p. cm.—(Land warfare; v.6)
Includes bibliographical references.
1. Military helicopters. I. Everett-Heath, E. J. II. Series.
UG1230.M56 1990 623.7'46047—dc20 89–48181

British Library Cataloguing in Publication Data
Military helicopters.
1. Military helicopters
I. Everett-Heath, E. J. II. Series
623.74'6047

ISBN 0–08–037341–0 Hardcover
ISBN 0–08–036716–x Flexicover

Printed in Great Britain by BPCC Wheatons Ltd., Exeter

Preface

This series of books is written for those who wish to improve their knowledge of military weapons and equipment. It is equally relevant to professional soldiers, those involved in developing and producing military weapons or indeed anyone interested in the art of modern warfare.

All the texts are written in a way which assumes no mathematical knowledge and no more technical depth than would be gleaned by any person who keeps himself or herself informed of developments in the modern world. It is intended that the books should be of particular interest to officers of the Armed Services wishing to further their professional knowledge as well as anyone involved in research, development, production, testing and maintenance of defence equipments.

The principal authors of the books are members of the Royal Military College of Science, Shrivenham, which is composed of a unique blend of academic and military experts. They are not only leaders in the technology of their subjects, but are aware of what the military practitioner needs to know. It is difficult to imagine any group of persons more fitted to write about the application of technology to the modern battlefield.

This Volume

The last two decades are reminiscent, in terms of the helicopter, of the 1930s' agonising over the role of the tank. However, military thinking has now moved beyond whether or not it will be of great influence. No one who practises or studies the art of modern warfare doubts that the helicopter has a major role to play on the battlefield: it makes little difference if it should be high or low intensity. The only differences of opinion lie in the question of how much it will dominate and the best way in which it can be used.

This book aims to give the reader both a sufficient technical background and a good understanding of the tactical roles. From this base it is hoped that he or she will be able to make an informed contribution to the discussions.

Acknowledgements

The authors greatly appreciate the help they have received from members of many service establishments. In particular from the Royal Aerospace Establishment, Farnborough, the Army Air Corps Centre and the Mechanics and Applied Thermodynamics Branches of the Royal Military College of Science. The authors are also most grateful to Mr W. Packer, Mr C. Smith and Mr R. Bending for their assistance with diagrams.

E.J.E-H.
G.M.M.
A.W.M.
K.E.R.

Contents

List of Illustrations   xi

List of Tables   xv

1. History   1

2. Roles   11

3. Principles of Flight   25

4. Power Plants and Transmissions   47

5. Avionics   59

6. The Helicopter as a Weapons Platform   77

7. Survivability   93

8. Advanced Features and Future Trends   111

9. Attack Helicopters   125

Self Test Questions   145

Answers to Self Test Questions   157

Glossary of Terms and Abbreviations   165

Bibliography   173

Index   175

List of Illustrations

Chapter 1 – History

Figure 1.1   Leonardo da Vinci's spiral   1
Figure 1.2   The Breguet–Richet Gyroplane No. 1   2
Figure 1.3   Paul Cornu's helicopter   3
Figure 1.4   The *Pescara No. 3*   4
Figure 1.5   The flapping hinge   5
Figure 1.6   The *Cierva C-6C* was the first autogiro to be built in Britain.
             It flew in 1926.   5
Figure 1.7   The FW-61 inside the Deutschlandhalle, Berlin, in 1937   7
Figure 1.8   The *Sikorsky R-4*   8
Figure 1.9   An *Alouette 2* in Army Air Corps service   9
Figure 1.10 A Bell AH-1G *Cobra*   9

Chapter 2 – Roles

Figure 2.1   A Soviet *Hind E* with four 57-mm rocket pods   13
Figure 2.2   An *Apache* with eight *Hellfire* missiles, a *Sidewinder* air-to-
             air missile on the starboard wing tip and a *Stinger* air-to-air
             missile on the port   13
Figure 2.3   *The Gazelle's* AF 532 observation sight   15
Figure 2.4   Heli-Tele on a *Lynx*   16
Figure 2.5   The *Lynx* can carry two *Milan* anti-tank missile teams   18
Figure 2.6   The mighty *Halo*   19
Figure 2.7   A *Sea King Mk 3* lowering its sonar   20
Figure 2.8   A Royal Navy *Lynx Mk 3* with four *Sea Skua* missiles   21
Figure 2.9   A French *Puma* with two *Exocet* missiles   21
Figure 2.10 A *Sea King Mk 2* modified to carry a *Searchwater* radar   22
Figure 2.11 An RAF SAR *Sea King* winches in a survivor   23

Chapter 3 – Principles of Flight

Figure 3.1   A typical rotor blade aerofoil section   27
Figure 3.2   The variation of lift and drag with incidence   28
Figure 3.3   Collective pitch control   29
Figure 3.4   A *Gazelle* swash plate   30
Figure 3.5   A feathering hinge   30
Figure 3.6   A typical tail rotor   31

Figure 3.7   The *Gazelle* fenestron   32
Figure 3.8   The rotor in forward flight   33
Figure 3.9   Flapping hinges   34
Figure 3.10 The *Lynx* semi-rigid rotor head   34
Figure 3.11 Motion of blade centre of gravity   35
Figure 3.12 Lag hinges   35
Figure 3.13 Forward transition   36
Figure 3.14 Cyclic pitch control using a swash plate   36
Figure 3.15 How a helicopter is controlled   37
Figure 3.16 A fully articulated rotor   38
Figure 3.17 An elastomeric rotor   39
Figure 3.18 The power required against forward speed for a typical
             helicopter   40
Figure 3.19 The speed differential across a rotor   42
Figure 3.20 Optimum tip speed and forward speed limitation   43
Figure 3.21 The effect of forward speed on helicopter load factor   43
Figure 3.22 A Soviet Mi-6 *Hook* with stub wings   44
Figure 3.23 The British *Rotodyne* compound helicopter   44
Figure 3.24 Possible configurations   45

Chapter 4 – Power Plants and Transmissions

Figure 4.1   Diagrammatic layout of a gas generator   48
Figure 4.2   Diagrammatic layout of a turbojet engine   48
Figure 4.3   Cross-section of a simple turbojet engine   49
Figure 4.4   Diagrammatic layout of a turboshaft engine   49
Figure 4.5   Cross-section of a turboshaft engine   49
Figure 4.6   Cross-section of a turbofan engine   50
Figure 4.7   Cross-section of a turboprop engine   50
Figure 4.8   Diagrammatic layout of a fixed turbine engine   50
Figure 4.9   Cross-section of a Turbomeca *Astazou* engine   51
Figure 4.10 Diagrammatic layout of a free turbine engine   51
Figure 4.11 Cross-section of a Rolls-Royce *Gnome* engine   52
Figure 4.12 Cross-section of a Rolls-Royce *Gem* engine   53
Figure 4.13 The *Gem* engine   53
Figure 4.14 The *RTM-322*   57

Chapter 5 – Avionics

Figure 5.1   AFCS trimmers in an Army *Lynx*   62
Figure 5.2   An Army *Lynx* instrument panel   63
Figure 5.3   A simple VSI   64
Figure 5.4   A flight director   66
Figure 5.5   A rate gyroscope used in a turn indicator   67
Figure 5.6   A direction indicator   68
Figure 5.7   The *RNS 252*   71
Figure 5.8   The dorsal radome houses the antenna for the *Sea Searcher*
             radar   72

Figure 5.9   The *Searchwater* radar   73
Figure 5.10 A modern MFD   74

Chapter 6 – The Helicopter as a Weapons Platform

Figure 6.1   The *Lynx* can carry eight TOW missiles   78
Figure 6.2   The *Havoc*'s 30-mm cannon fully deflected 110° to port   79
Figure 6.3   The *Apache*'s 30-mm chain gun   80
Figure 6.4   70-mm rocket pods on a *Black Hawk*   81
Figure 6.5   A French Army *Gazelle* fires a HOT missile   82
Figure 6.6   A *Havoc* with eight *Spiral* anti-tank missile tubes and a pod
             for 20 × 80-mm rockets   83
Figure 6.7   An *Apache* with eight *Hellfire* missiles and 38 × 70 mm
             rockets   84
Figure 6.8   A *Hind E* with, from left to right, an empty pylon, an 80-mm
             rocket pod, a 57-mm rocket pod and a bomb   85
Figure 6.9   The Italian A-129 *Mangusta*   86
Figure 6.10 A West German Army *Bo-105* with six HOT missiles   88
Figure 6.11 The mast-mounted sight of the *OH-58D*   89

Chapter 7 – Survivability

Figure 7.1   The *Hind*'s sight is the larger assembly under the forward
             cockpit on the starboard side   94
Figure 7.2   A mast-mounted sight reduces exposure   95
Figure 7.3   The latest versions of the *Cobra* have a flat plate canopy   96
Figure 7.4   Rotor downwash   96
Figure 7.5   The swept rotor blade tip and canted tail rotor of the *Black Hawk*   97
Figure 7.6   Exhaust gas suppressors on a *Lynx*   99
Figure 7.7   The forward radar warning antennae on a Royal Navy *Lynx*   101
Figure 7.8   Wire cutters above and below the cockpit of a Swedish Army
             OH-58   102
Figure 7.9   Most helicopter IR jammers are located above the forward end
             of the tailboom   104
Figure 7.10 The *Apache* has well separated engines   105
Figure 7.11 Extra armour plate has been added to protect the cockpit sides of
             this *Hind F*   106
Figure 7.12 The crashworthy troop seats in a *Black Hawk*   108

Chapter 8 – Advanced Features and Future Trends

Figure 8.1   Trends in engine fuel consumption and weight for a given
             power   112
Figure 8.2   A BERP main rotor blade   113
Figure 8.3   The pre-production ASP blade on an *EH-101*   113
Figure 8.4   The Sikorsky/US Army *S-75* ACAP demonstrator   114
Figure 8.5   The use of non-metallic materials   115

Figure 8.6   Down flow through the helicopter rotor in the hover   116
Figure 8.7   The production of side force by the Coanda effect   116
Figure 8.8   A helicopter fitted with the NOTAR device   117
Figure 8.9   The lift distribution on the rotors of the ABC aircraft   117
Figure 8.10 The comparison of load factor on ABC and conventional
             helicopters   118
Figure 8.11 The ABC demonstrator vehicle in flight   118
Figure 8.12 The reduced length of the ABC   119
Figure 8.13 A comparison of load factors   119
Figure 8.14 The V-22 *Osprey*   120
Figure 8.15 The instrument panel of a Royal Navy *Commando* Mk2   123

Chapter 9 – Attack Helicopters

Figure 9.1   The AH-1G *Cobra*   126
Figure 9.2   A USMC AH-IW equipped with *Hellfire* missiles and a
             20-mm cannon.   128
Figure 9.3   A twin-engined AH-1W *SuperCobra*   129
Figure 9.4   A pair of *Apaches* each with eight *Hellfire* and 38 × 70-mm
             rockets   130
Figure 9.5   Potential air-to-air missiles for the *Apache* displayed at the
             Paris Air Show in 1989   132
Figure 9.6   The PNVS is mounted above the TADS   133
Figure 9.7   The AAWWS   135
Figure 9.8   The *Apache's* 'quiet' scissors tail rotor   136
Figure 9.9   The *Mangusta* armed with TOW missiles   137
Figure 9.10 A TOW missile being launched from a *Mangusta*   139
Figure 9.11 The *Hind A* with its side-by-side pilot seating and single-
             barrelled nose gun   140
Figure 9.12 A *Hind D* displaying two rails for *Swatter* missiles, 57-mm
             rocket pods and a four-barrelled 12.7-mm gun in a turret
             under the nose   141
Figure 9.13 The distinctive H-frame missile rails on this *Hind E* can be
             clearly seen   142
Figure 9.14 The *Hind F* has a 30-mm cannon fixed to the starboard side
             of the fuselage instead of a turret-mounted Gatling gun   143

List of Tables

Table 3.1   The International Standard Atmosphere   26
Table 6.1   Missile Characteristics   90
Table 9.1   Attack Helicopter Characteristics   144

1.

History

The Early Days

Men have dreamed of being able to fly since time immemorial. Unable to imagine the fixed-wing aircraft of this century, they believed, not unnaturally, that the solution lay in emulating birds. If they could construct wings strong yet light enough for them to flap, they would be able to leave the ground and fly without any forward run. As we know, flapping wings turned out to be a nightmare rather than a dream. But the ingenuity of man knows few bounds and ultimately triumphed with a machine whose wings rotated rather than flapped.

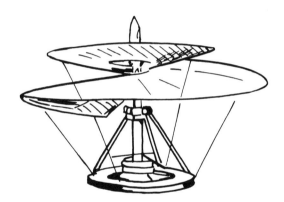

Fig. 1.1 Leonardo da Vinci's spiral

Received wisdom gives the credit for imagining that man might fly by means of an airscrew to Leonardo da Vinci. In the 1480s he drew sketches of a 'helicopter', a corkscrew spiral rotor to be made with wood and starched linen and driven by a simple spring mechanism. The intention was that the device would screw itself vertically into the air; it is doubtful, however, that it ever flew or was even built. If any progress were made in the development of the helicopter during the next 300 years we know nothing about it. A Russian, Mikhail Lomonosov, allegedly demonstrated his model before the Russian Academy of Sciences in July 1754, but it was the Frenchmen, Launoy and Bienvenu, who claimed to have been the first to have flown a self-propelled model helicopter. In April 1784 it amazed the French Academy of Sciences by soaring up to the ceiling of their great hall. Many other enthusiasts devoted considerable time and energy to heavier-than-air flight in the 19th century, one of the most successful being Sir George Cayley. Revered as the

1

'Father of British Aeronautics', he was the first man to approach the problems methodically and to appreciate how they might be overcome. It was sometime during the mid-19th century that the Viscomte de Ponton d'Amecourt coined the word helicopter, a combination of the Greek words *helix* (spiral) and *pteron* (wing).

A vital milestone was reached in 1842 when Horatio Phillips flew the first model aircraft – and a helicopter at that – that was powered by a steam engine rather than by springs or other devices. But the breakthrough came in 1876 when N. A. Otto invented the four-stroke internal combustion engine, the first engine to use liquid fuel. By 1885 a practicable engine with an acceptable power-to-weight ratio had been built and it was only a matter of time before the first man-carrying powered flight would be achieved.

The First Flight

The Wright brothers made their historic flight – the world's first powered, sustained and controlled flight – on 17 December 1903. On 19 September 1907 the first piloted helicopter, the Breguet–Richet Gyroplane No. 1, lifted from the ground at Douai in France. It was powered by a 45-hp Antoinette engine which drove four biplane rotor systems, each with four blades, thus giving 32 lifting surfaces. It rose to a height of 60 cm (2 ft), but since it had no controls save an engine throttle it had to be steadied by a man at each corner; thus it could not receive the credit for being the first helicopter to make a truly free flight.

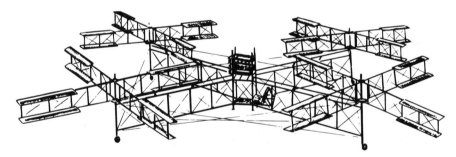

Fig. 1.2 The Breguet–Richet Gyroplane No. 1

That achievement was claimed by another Frenchman, Paul Cornu, who made the first free flight in a helicopter at Coquanvilliers on 13 November 1907. At the centre of a *V*-frame on a four-wheeled undercarriage were Cornu and a 24-hp Antoinette engine. At each end of the *V* was mounted a belt-driven wheel to which were attached two fabric-skinned blades. Fore and aft control planes did little to improve control and this machine subsided into the sands of history after about fifteen very short flights.

Engine power may have been harnessed but lack of stability and control posed serious problems and the way ahead was far from clear. It had been recognised for some time that when a rotor is turned by an engine mounted in a fuselage then a reaction in the form of the fuselage turning in the opposite direction is set up in accordance with Newton's Third Law: to every action there is an equal and

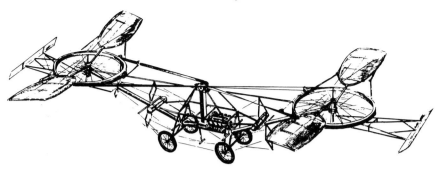

FIG. 1.3 Paul Cornu's helicopter

opposite reaction. Various methods were devised to overcome this torque reaction. The most popular was the use of contra-rotating rotors on co-axial or individual shafts, when the two torque reactions cancelled each other out. In 1874 a German, Achenbach, produced a design which included a tail rotor for anti-torque control, a device that was to become more or less standard. It was also discovered that if the power for the main rotor blades was provided at the tips of the blades, rather than driving them through a control shaft, then no torque was experienced. Consequently a number of designs, ranging from steam jets or compressed air to small driving propellers, used devices placed at the ends of the main blades. Although these ideas removed the need for any anti-torque measures the method of getting energy continuously to the rotor tips was complex and difficult and, at this time, too great a challenge. In 1912, however, a Russian, Boris Yuriev, was the first man actually to build a helicopter with a single main rotor and an anti-torque rotor, a step into the unknown but one that was to be followed by nearly all helicopters built world-wide to the present day. Unfortunately the machine failed to complete its ground tests and never flew.

Directional control and transition into forward flight posed special problems. Early solutions were to tilt the main rotors in a fixed position to give both vertical lift and horizontal movement, or for the pilot to tilt the main shafts by means of cables. In 1912 Jakob Ellehammer, a Dane, designed and flew a helicopter which incorporated a simple form of cyclic pitch control, invented in 1906 by an Italian, G. A. Crocco, which allowed Ellehammer to have some control of the lift from his two co-axial rotors.

The early 1920s saw several interesting projects of which the most promising was the Marquis de Pescara's third helicopter, known as the No. 3. Though a ponderous and awkward-looking machine it represented a major step forward in helicopter technology: the eight pairs of blades in its contra-rotating system could be controlled in flight to produce increased lift and the rotor head could be tilted to generate forward flight. Although only modest speeds were achieved, this aircraft was the first to give a convincing demonstration of the controlling of both lift and direction of flight. Pescara also showed that he was one of the first to understand autorotation, since his aircraft was designed to descend safely should the engine fail. Pescara had a rival in Etienne Oehmichen who managed to complete the world's first 1-km (0.62-miles) closed-circuit flight in May 1924. It is surely

Fig. 1.4 The Pescara No. 3

astonishing that it took over 16 years from the first flight for a helicopter to achieve that distance, which took 7 minutes 40 seconds, a speed of 8 kph (5 mph). The machine was actually able to remain airborne for 14 minutes. Despite this success the Oehmichen No. 2 was not in the same class as the Pescara No. 3 which represented the best in helicopter technology at the time.

Juan de la Cierva

In any discussion about helicopter development the name of the Spaniard Juan de la Cierva will always be mentioned, although he never designed, built nor flew a helicopter. Spurred on by the driving desire to build an aircraft that did not stall, he came to the conclusion that if he could build a machine whose wings were able to, and did, rotate freely at all times then the danger of stalling would be eliminated. To a fixed-wing aircraft he added a lifting rotor which was kept spinning purely by air flowing through it as a consequence of the aircraft's forward speed. The rotor was not driven by an engine and therefore the problem of torque did not arise. This invention he called an autogiro.

With an unpowered rotor and the functions of lift and propulsion separated Cierva's machines were unable to hover nor, initially, take-off vertically. However, they were much less complicated than a helicopter and a good deal safer than a fixed-wing aircraft at slow speed or when the engine failed. Then they could autorotate; that is, still derive lift from the air flowing through the rotor and thus achieve a slower rate of descent.

Cierva's first three autogiros, begun in 1920, were failures. Cierva was quick to realise that the problem lay with his rotor, the blades of which were rigidly attached to the rotor hub. This gave rise to the problem of unequal lift from the blades, a matter covered in more detail in Chapter 3.

Cierva solved the problem by inserting a hinge between the rotor hub and each blade. It was known as the flapping hinge and its invention was a major contribu-

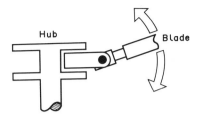

FIG. 1.5 The flapping hinge

tion to the development of rotary-wing aircraft. Cierva's fourth design, the C.4, made a successful maiden flight in Spain in January 1923. Cierva also found that his rotor blades needed freedom to move in the plane of rotation and to provide this he invented the drag hinge.

In October 1925 Cierva brought one of his autogiros to England at the invitation of the Air Ministry, and in January 1926 two were ordered for RAF trials. Cierva remained in England to carry out research and development until his premature death in December 1936. In the meantime one of his designs, the C.8L Mk 2, had made the first crossing of the English Channel by a rotary-wing aircraft on 18 September 1928. The Royal Navy undertook autogiro trials at sea, the Army used them to see if artillery officers, flying as passengers, could engage ground targets using normal gunnery procedures and the RAF employed them for radar calibration duties during the Second World War. While the autogiro had few vices, very

FIG. 1.6 The Cierva C-6C was the first autogiro to be built in Britain; it flew in June 1926 (*RAF Museum*)

good lookout and a comparatively wide speed range, it could not hover and no autogiro that ever flew could carry more than one pilot and one passenger. Therefore in the 1940s it was not considered to have much military application, and despite studies more recently this perception has not changed. Nevertheless, Cierva's contribution to rotary-wing aviation has been an enduring one.

The 1930s

Helicopter progress was still agonisingly slow: in October 1930 the Italian d'Ascanio helicopter set a new world altitude record of just 18 m (59 ft); given that helicopters had been flying for 23 years this height was remarkable in its mediocrity and demonstrated convincingly the complexities of helicopter flight. At last in 1936 the German Focke-Wulf FW-61 appeared and the following year it smashed all existing records. A machine with twin rotors on outriggers and an engine-cooling propeller, which led some people to believe that it was an autogiro, the FW-61 made the first ever helicopter autorotational landing in May 1937 and a month later set five records for altitude (2,439 m; 8,002 ft), endurance (1 hour 20 minutes), speed (122.55 kph; 76.15 mph), distance (80.6 km; 50 miles) and distance in a straight line (16.4 km; 10.2 miles). In January 1939 the FW-61 flew 230 km (143 miles) without stopping and ascended to 3,427 m (11,243 ft), thus proving itself to be the first truly practical helicopter.

The Second World War prevented large-scale production of any German helicopters and it was left to Igor Sikorsky, the greatest helicopter pioneer of them all, to design in the USA the helicopter which was the first in the world to enter series production: in 1944 the two-seat R-4 with a single main rotor and single tail rotor started to roll off the line in large numbers for the American armed forces and the RAF. The age of the helicopter had dawned – but it was an age that initially was recognised by few. As four-engined bombers carried heavy ordnance loads over long distances in Europe and the Far East, helicopters had no role at all save the odd casualty evacuation flight in the Far East. The first twin-engined helicopter, the Soviet 2 MG Omega, made a few tentative flights in early 1943 but this line of development led nowhere.

After the Second World War

The military value of helicopters became apparent only in the 1950s when the British used them sparingly in Malaya, Cyprus and during the short-lived Suez campaign; the Americans in Korea and the French in Indo-China and Algeria used them more widely. Although the tasks performed by these aircraft were mainly observation and reconnaissance, casualty evacuation and the carriage of commanders and light supplies, their use as weapons platforms was also being investigated. As a means of mobile firepower the helicopter was attractive but acceptance of this apparently rather esoteric vehicle of war was still slow: critics dwelled on its alleged vulnerability and inability to operate at night or in bad weather, its poor load-carrying capability and its complex maintenance and burdensome logistic support.

In December 1949 a helicopter with a new shape flew. The Sikorsky S-55

FIG. 1.7 The FW-61 inside the Deutschlandhalle, Berlin, in 1937 (*Museum of Army Flying*)

FIG. 1.8 The Sikorsky R-4 (*P. G. Harrison*)

(*Whirlwind* in British service) was basically a box directly underneath the main rotor and with a wheel at each corner. The beauty of this was that the box, or cabin, was at the centre of gravity of the helicopter and therefore much greater loads than previously could be carried given the required engine power; furthermore, the balance or trim of the helicopter was much simplified whatever the load or amount of fuel on board. To permit this configuration the engine was positioned in the nose. The techniques of load-carrying were taken a step further when the Russians produced the Mil Mi-4 *Hound* with clamshell rear-loading doors which permitted vehicles to drive up into the cabin.

The next technical breakthrough was the advent of the turbine engine, first flown in a helicopter in December 1951. It offered many advantages over the piston engine. A vastly improved power-to-weight ratio allowed a smaller, lighter and therefore cheaper helicopter to be built for a specified role. A much wider range of turbine fuels could be used instead of expensive high octane gasoline. Because of its size and weight it could be located close to the main rotor hub and thus simplify the transmission. The first production helicopter with a turbine engine was the French *Alouette* 2 which made its maiden flight in March 1955; it was to play a major role in Algeria where it was armed with a variety of weapons including air-to-ground missiles.

The war in Vietnam provided the United States with a situation and terrain which were well suited to helicopter operations. Medium and heavy-lift helicopters and the ubiquitous utility helicopter, the UH-1 *Huey*, all played important parts in

FIG. 1.9 An *Alouette* 2 in Army Air Corps service (*Museum of Army Flying*)

FIG. 1.10 A Bell AH-1G *Cobra* (*US Army*)

this war. But perhaps it was the introduction of the dedicated attack helicopter, the AH-1 *Cobra*, which arrived in Vietnam in September 1967, that carried with it the greatest implications. Popularly known as gunships, these helicopters were armed with a variety of weapons: miniguns, cannon, grenade launchers, free flight rockets and, latterly, missiles. They made their presence felt as soon as they started combat operations. The ratio of helicopter losses to sorties flown in Vietnam confounded the critics; even enthusiasts were surprised at how many hits a helicopter could take and still keep flying.

Since Vietnam the helicopter has confirmed its place as an indispensable weapon of war. In conflicts in Africa, the Falklands, during the Israeli invasion of Lebanon, the Iran–Iraq war, in Northern Ireland and elsewhere it has proved its worth, and nowhere more so than in Afghanistan where the Mil Mi-8 *Hip* and Mi-24 *Hind* in particular made a strong impact on the fighting.

The two major blocs, NATO and the Warsaw Pact, have equipped their forces with large numbers of several types of helicopter. Tactical and technical development is continuous and quickening and has brought the helicopter to where it is today: the most versatile vehicle in military service.

2.

Roles

The first military helicopters were used for casualty evacuation, the carriage of senior commanders and for observation. Since those days – the latter stages of the Second World War – they have been put to an ever wider variety of tasks, all in some way using their special characteristics: a comparatively wide speed range, the ability to hover and to make use of the terrain to aid concealment and achieve surprise, role flexibility and good communications. The helicopter's great attraction is that it can ignore all terrain obstacles (although mountains impose some limitations), including minefields and routes and areas blocked by refugees or which have been sabotaged or chemically contaminated.

The extent to which the helicopter can enhance mobility on the battlefield will have an impact as great as that exerted by the advent of the tank on trench warfare.

Limitations

While helicopters have certain unique capabilities they, like all battlefield systems, have their limitations. These are often over-emphasised with the result that helicopters are not always fully exploited; on the other hand, it is important that these limitations are recognised and understood.

Modern helicopters have navigation aids and instruments to permit flight in cloud. But the lack of ground-based aids and obstacle warning devices precludes their flying in fog and when visibility is poor. The lack of an anti- or de-icing capability also prevents some of them from flying in certain low-temperature conditions. Darkness inevitably degrades the ability to carry out some tasks, although the introduction of night-vision devices has already done much, and will do more, to enhance a night fighting and flying capability.

Helicopters have a limited endurance and therefore should not be deployed on their tasks too soon or they will have to break off early to refuel. Endurance is sometimes affected by the payload; then fuel has to be traded off for armaments, passengers or freight. The requirements for fuel, munitions and spare parts impose a considerable load on the logistic services.

The vulnerability of helicopters has generated a good deal of uninformed opinion. Combat action in Vietnam, Afghanistan and elsewhere has shown that helicopters are not easy to hit and even when hit do not necessarily stop flying. If they do make a forced landing, successful or otherwise, they can often be recovered and repaired. The design and construction of a helicopter, the warning devices and countermeasures incorporated and the flying tactics used all play a part in minimising vulnerability. This is such an important aspect of military helicopters that it is treated separately in Chapter 7.

In most armies now the combat helicopter is regarded as an item of ground forces equipment which operates in a land environment as part of an all-arms formation. In general terms, helicopters have been designed to fight, to look and to carry and, while doing one or more of these, to communicate.

Attack

This role embodies the application of firepower using on-board weapons of all types. It has now established itself as the most important role for the helicopter within NATO and the Warsaw Pact. The term 'armed action' used by the British Army Air Corps for many years involves the attack of tanks and certain other vehicles in their support.

The principal target is enemy armoured fighting vehicles, specifically self-propelled air-defence systems, tanks with mine ploughs, main battle tanks and command vehicles. Guided missiles, the most modern with ranges as great as 5 km, are the preferred weapons as they allow the helicopter to remain beyond the range of its opponent's weapons and because they have the highest probability of achieving a kill. NATO defensive tactics involve acquiring and engaging targets from concealed ambush positions while the helicopter is in the hover or moving very slowly. Warsaw Pact tactics are quite different: their helicopters fly above the treetops at speeds up to about 250 kph (155 mph) and then ascend to permit a shallow dive on to the target before launching their weapons at close to maximum range.

Some attack helicopters carry other weapons besides missiles with which to engage soft-skinned or lightly armoured point targets or area targets. Soviet *Hinds*, for example, carry 57-mm or 80-mm free flight rockets while the American *Apache* is armed with 70-mm rockets. Both are also armed with 30-mm cannon although some *Hinds* have a four-barrelled 12.7-mm machine gun. Grenade launchers and bombs are carried occasionally by Soviet helicopters.

It is now generally regarded as inevitable that when opposing helicopters meet on the battlefield in support of their own ground forces they will engage each other. This type of engagement may be followed in due course by helicopters actually being tasked to search out and fight enemy helicopters. To cater for this specific task a helicopter should be armed, ideally, with a supersonic agile missile for long-range engagements and a quick reaction weapon for short-range self-defence. Originally designed as a shoulder-launched surface-to-air missile, the American *Stinger* is now being installed on some American helicopters.

As a means of mobile firepower the helicopter is unequalled. With its good communications it can undertake one task while being on call for another in a completely different sector of the battlefield (its endurance permitting). In an anti-tank role helicopters *en masse* are usually more effective in achieving shock impact than when used in small numbers; but there will often be occasions when just a few helicopters rapidly deployed at a critical moment can achieve the desired effect. Larger numbers of helicopters are more likely to be detected before they can

FIG. 2.1 A Soviet *Hind* E with four 57-mm rocket pods

FIG. 2.2 An *Apache* with eight *Hellfire* missiles, a *Sidewinder* air-to-air missile on the starboard wing tip and a *Stinger* air-to-air missile on the port (*McDonnell Douglas*)

open fire, however, and if they are to remain concealed for as long as possible a very large amount of terrain is needed to provide sufficient cover.

Reconnaissance, Observation and Target Acquisition

Observation and reconnaissance were two of the original roles for the helicopter and they are still among the most difficult if the crew are in contact with the enemy and are to be successful at seeing without being detected, visually, aurally, on radar or by other devices. Observation and reconnaissance may be visual, photographic or electronic. They may be undertaken with passengers or on behalf of ground personnel and have many aspects: from shadowing an enemy armoured penetration to taking engineers on a minefield, route or bridge reconnaissance; from enabling a commander to have a quick look at the ground that he is to defend, to maintaining surveillance on an exposed flank or a gap in the obstacle belt. Helicopters may also take part in radiac and chemical survey.

The recognition and acquisition of targets are important tasks for reconnaissance or scout helicopters. If they are achieved without being seen and successfully 'handed over' to the helicopters that are to carry out the attack, then surprise will be complete, destruction will be more likely and the risk of sustaining losses or damage to one's own force lessened. Attack helicopters are precious assets, expensive to procure and therefore usually present in insufficient numbers; it is thus not usually considered wise to send them out to find their own targets.

Reconnaissance is not always by stealth; indeed, Warsaw Pact helicopters quite often undertake overt reconnaissance with *Hind* attack helicopters. This armed reconnaissance sometimes achieves its results by fire to provoke a reaction from the enemy. In NATO terms, armed reconnaissance signifies the searching for and selective destruction of specific targets by the same helicopter.

Good optical aids help enormously. The days of hand-held binoculars, both standard and stabilised, will soon be gone. Already many reconnaissance helicopters have sights, usually installed in the roof, like the AF 532 in the *Gazelle*; in the American OH-58D, however, the sight is mounted above the main rotor.

Observation sights are stabilised and have two fields of view and two magnifications: typically × 2.5 and a comparatively wide field of view for searching, and × 10 for a narrow field of view to track the target. Included in such sights may be a laser rangefinder, laser target-marker and thermal imaging, depending on the funds available, and space and weight constraints. A roof-mounted sight is better than a nose-mounted sight both ergonomically and as far as exposure to the enemy and therefore survivability of the helicopter are concerned. The least exposure is achieved by having a mast-mounted sight because, in theory, the entire helicopter except for the sight can be kept hidden; in practice, it is not simple to hover to such precision and the cover in front of the helicopter is rarely uniformally level. Nevertheless, studies have shown that mast-mounted sights offer a 17% increase in survivability when compared with helicopters with roof-mounted sights and 50% when compared with helicopters with nose-mounted sights.

Other observation devices, mainly for use in internal security operations, may be installed. An example is the colour TV camera, known as Heli-Tele, mounted externally in a gyrostabilised sphere assembly, on the port side of the *Lynx*. It is

Fig. 2.3 The *Gazelle* AF 532 observation sight (*E. J. Everett-Heath*)

remotely controlled by the co-pilot and a 5-in TV screen is located on the instrument panel between the two pilots to assist in aiming the camera and to give some measure of surveillance from the air. The camera has a zoom capability and considerable freedom of movement in azimuth and elevation. A number of ground stations can receive the picture and any spoken commentary. The ability of the camera to zoom in for close-ups of specific targets is of particular benefit to ground observers who can interpret the information well away from the scene of action and order whatever counter-action may be necessary. This TV has proved very successful in monitoring traffic movement, civil disturbances and riots. Hand-held cameras may also be used from helicopters but only with lenses up to 200 mm or so.

For night operations searchlights are useful and for covert illumination they may have an infra-red filter. More effective, but much more expensive, is a thermal-imaging sight which can be fitted internally or externally. Night vision goggles are not really an aid to observation or target acquisition given their comparatively short range. They are used principally to help in flying the aircraft at night.

Direction of Fire

The adjustment of artillery fire was an early role for Army aircraft. Really a combination of the application of firepower and observation, this role has been expanded to include the direction of all kinds of fire: artillery, mortar, tank and naval guns. Helicopter crews are trained in the appropriate procedures but, when

FIG. 2.4 Heli-Tele on a *Lynx* (*Westland Helicopters*)

necessary, artillery forward observation officers and mortar fire-controllers can be carried. Observation of the fall of shot is rarely easy and rounds which land in dead ground cause complications. Successful shoots often depend on the good training and experience of the crew.

The direction of fighter aircraft on to their ground targets is also well-suited to helicopter crews who can move more quickly than any ground vehicle to the best vantage point and who have with them good air-to-air and air-to-ground communications. Laser target-marking is beginning to supersede the older methods of a purely verbal description of the target, smoke grenades and signal flares.

The roles described above may be termed combat, or in-contact roles. But helicopters are equally adept at undertaking combat support or out-of-contact roles.

Command and Control

Fighting a battle from a helicopter will not always be desirable nor to every commander's liking. However, helicopters can be fitted out to act as airborne command posts – and, indeed, the Russians, in particular, have converted a considerable number of Mi-6 *Hook* and Mi-8 *Hip* helicopters for this role. They carry extra radio sets, some with secure speech facilities and extra staff to man them. Such command posts are essential for airmobile operations, particularly if a crossing of the forward edge of battle area (FEBA) is envisaged.

Helicopters may be used as airborne radio relay or re-broadcast stations and also as traffic-control posts.

To assist in the whole process of command and control, commanders may employ helicopters as airborne rovers and to bring members of reconnaissance and orders groups to their headquarters (HQ). The work of staff officers and liaison officers can often be eased by using helicopters instead of ground transport. During periods of electronic silence helicopters can be invaluable in carrying information between HQs.

It has been recognised for some years now that the side which controls the electromagnetic spectrum has a decided advantage. Thus electronic warfare has received much attention and helicopters have their part, not only in providing protection for themselves but more positively in disrupting enemy systems. Direction finding of HQ and command posts is important as is the jamming of enemy fire-control radars for air-defence systems, early warning and ground-control intercept radars and the jamming of communications links.

Tactical Support

As weapons can be moved about the battlefield so can troops and supplies be carried quickly and easily from point to point. The scale of the lift depends on the size and payload of the helicopters involved and on the numbers of aircraft available. In the British Armed Forces the *Lynx*, without its missiles, can lift nine combat-equipped troops, the *Puma* 16 and the *Chinook* 33. In a critical situation these numbers could be increased. Any helicopter able to carry personnel can also carry casualties and most can accept stretchers locked into position. The *Lynx* and even the Soviet *Hind* can each take four stretchers. Although not a specific role, casualty evacuation is a task gladly undertaken by aircrew. The knowledge that helicopters will be tasked whenever possible to evacuate casualties provides a major boost to the morale of the troops in contact with the enemy; countless lives have been saved since the Second World War in many campaigns round the world.

The Americans and Russians have pioneered the use of helicopters in airmobile and air assault operations. Other countries have been slow to follow; but the tide may be turning and more airmobile battalions and brigades will certainly form within NATO and the Warsaw Pact in the next decade. They will not necessarily have organic helicopters, although this is the ideal. Such units are usually tasked to capture bridges or selected river crossing-points, dominating ground, HQs, communications centres or even airfields a few kilometres ahead of the advancing ground forces. Heliborne troops are less vulnerable than parachutists and are more likely to land exactly where planned. The troop-carrying helicopters, flying over enemy-held territory, need to be escorted by attack helicopters and probably by fixed-wing fighters as well; transport helicopters lifting support weapons, ammunition and vehicles will bring up the rear.

Fig. 2.5 The *Lynx* can carry two *Milan* anti-tank missile teams (*Westland Helicopters*)

Tactical transport helicopters, even armed helicopters with a small cabin, can contribute to the armour battle by deploying infantry anti-tank teams to different parts of the battlefield to counter local penetrations.

The laying of smoke screens and minefields can be accomplished quite easily by helicopters. Anti-tank and anti-personnel mines can be laid by means of a parachute or dispensed from a container while the helicopter hover-taxis a few metres above the ground.

Logistic Support

The resupply of ammunition, fuel and stores, such as medical equipment and critical spare parts, sometimes becomes urgent. During the Falklands conflict, for example, the carriage forward of artillery and small arms ammunition became critical. Consumption rates of field artillery could only be met by using helicopter resupply. Resupply by parachute has now all but been superseded by the helicopter, except where long distances are involved.

In Vietnam the Americans pioneered the recovery of aircraft and helicopters that had been shot down or forced to land by using large helicopters to lift them back to base as an underslung load. Many were salvaged and repaired to fly again. Millions of dollars were thereby saved.

Underslinging loads of all kinds is often the quickest and most convenient way of transporting particularly awkward or bulky items, such as artillery or missile systems. There are dangers and difficulties associated with the hook-up of underslung loads and in flying with them. If care is not taken the load may oscillate and endanger the helicopter itself and possibly result in premature jettisoning.

Fig. 2.6 The mighty *Halo* (*E. J. Everett-Heath*)

The Russians lead the world in the production of heavy lift helicopters. The biggest is the Mi-26 *Halo* which is capable of taking a load of 20,000 kg (44,100 lb) in its hold or as an underslung load. All types of equipment, weapon systems and vehicles can be carried in the hold which has space for as many as 99 seated troops, or perhaps as many as 150 without seating.

Naval Roles

Naval helicopters exploit the unique capabilities of the helicopter in much the same way as their land-based counterparts. Their roles include anti-submarine and anti-surface warfare, airborne early-warning, tactical support and logistic tasks.

Anti-Submarine Warfare (ASW)

This is the primary role of the naval helicopter. Operating from dedicated aircraft carriers or smaller ships, such as frigates, anti-submarine helicopters of various types play a vital role in combined air, surface and sub-surface anti-submarine operations. ASW helicopters in a surface force enlarge the area of defence against submarines substantially. Unlike fixed-wing aircraft, particu-

FIG. 2.7 A *Sea King* Mk 3 lowering its sonar (*Rolls-Royce*)

larly shore-based ones, helicopters can be deployed very rapidly against sub-marine threats and they are less affected by adverse weather conditions.

By virtue of their ability to hover, helicopters can use dipping sonar, an acoustic device which can be lowered to the depth of water most suitable for detection and where it is unencumbered by the hull and water-flow noises associated with ship-mounted or towed sonars. More flexible than expendable sonobuoys, dipping sonar nevertheless has its disadvantages: when it is dipping the helicopter is in the hover and therefore using a great deal of fuel and is a stationary target. When changing its position a helicopter must raise its sonar from the water and break contact. Thus helicopters usually work in pairs – one holding the contact while the other moves. Nevertheless, ASW helicopters can move and redeploy their sonars rapidly, dipping in a random and unpredictable manner to the general detriment of enemy submarine operations.

Submarines can also be detected by a helicopter's radar even if only an antenna, periscope or snorkel is exposed; these can sometimes be picked up at very long ranges. Another piece of equipment in common service is the magnetic anomaly detector (MAD) which detects the distortion in the earth's magnetic field caused by the large metal hull of a submarine. A MAD has only a very short range and is more often used to establish the course and speed of the target once it has been acquired.

The submarine, having been located, can be attacked by a helicopter-launched acoustic torpedo, impact with the water being reduced by a parachute. Depth charges are less favoured as they offer a smaller chance of achieving a kill.

Anti-Surface Warfare (ASUW)

As with ASW, ASUW operations follow the same pattern of search, detect, identify and attack. Radar is the primary acquisition aid and guided missiles the attack weapons. The helicopter must endeavour not to be detected itself by the surface force. This can be achieved by low-level flight, but such a method of operation reduces the helicopter's radar range. Whatever height is flown the aim is to detect, identify the target and launch the anti-ship missile outside the range of the target ship's defensive weapon systems. Much therefore depends on the type of missile used. The *Lynx* with its *Seaspray* radar is too small a helicopter to carry large missiles and so it is equipped with comparatively short-range *Sea Skua* missiles with semi-active homing heads. Larger helicopters, such as the *Sea King* and EH-101, may have larger and heavier missiles, such as the *Sea Eagle*, *Exocet* or *Harpoon* with inertial guidance and active radar terminal homing.

FIG. 2.8 A Royal Navy *Lynx* Mk 3 with four *Sea Skua* missiles (*Westland Helicopters*)

FIG. 2.9 A French *Puma* with two *Exocet* missiles (*E. J. Everett-Heath*)

Over-the-Horizon Targeting

To extend the engagement range of a ship's missiles and therefore to enhance its survivability, data on a surface target can be supplied by a helicopter flying well away from both. This procedure allows ships to attack targets out of radar range over the horizon. Once the missile is launched the helicopter can provide mid-course guidance.

Airborne Early Warning (AEW)

The need for AEW for the fleet has always been recognised but for a time it had been thought that British naval operations would always be carried out within range of land-based air support. The Falklands war quickly proved the fallacy of that theory. If carriers with AEW fixed-wing aircraft were not available then AEW would have to be carried out by helicopters.

To meet this urgent operational requirement in 1982 a few Royal Navy *Sea Kings* were equipped to carry a modified *Searchwater* surveillance radar with the antenna housed in a large, inflatable dome on the starboard side of the fuselage. Depending on the *Sea King*'s patrol height, targets can be detected at ranges which give the surface fleet time to take whatever action is deemed necessary.

FIG. 2.10 A *Sea King* Mk 2 modified to carry a *Searchwater* radar (*Westland Helicopters*)

Tactical Support

While land-based helicopters can lay mines, certain types of naval helicopter are used for mine-sweeping. The Americans with the MH-53E *Sea Dragon* and the Russians with the Mi-14 *Haze* B are the leading proponents of this activity.

Naval helicopters are one of the means of getting marines, their support weapons, vehicles and other equipment ashore and then building up the force as quickly as possible in terms of men and supplies. The helicopters may be supported by fixed-wing aircraft and armed helicopters, operated by the marines themselves.

FIG. 2.11 An RAF SAR *Sea King* winches in a survivor (*Westland Helicopters*)

Returning helicopters can bring casualties back to the medical facilities aboard ship.

Search and rescue (SAR) on some occasions can be classed as tactical support. Naval and air force helicopters have been used in this role for many years, saving numerous military and civil personnel at sea and on coastlines. In wartime the crews of disabled and sinking ships and downed aircrew will draw the attention of any available helicopters. Often undertaken in appalling weather conditions, SAR demands courage and skill of a high order on the part of every member of the crew.

Logistic Support

Vertrep, or vertical replenishment, is the naval term for resupply by helicopter from one ship to another while they are both underway. Loads are usually underslung. It is not only stores that can be transferred but also, of course, personnel.

Military helicopters have demonstrated many times their versatility and shown how they can influence events on the battlefield and at sea. As their capabilities have expanded so has the variety of their roles. But there is little doubt that their full potential has not yet been fully exploited.

3.

Principles of Flight

Hovering Flight

A pure helicopter is an aircraft which is supported in flight by an essentially horizontal rotor which is external to the vehicle.

The Actuator Disc

A conceptual understanding of many aspects of the helicopter rotor can be obtained by considering that rotor to be replaced by an imaginary disc of the same diameter and in the plane of the rotor: it is called an actuator disc. This disc, through which the air passes without hindrance, simultaneously causes this air to increase in static pressure. The static pressure below the disc is therefore higher than the static pressure above it. The resulting pressure difference, acting on the imaginary disc, causes a force at right angles to the plane of the disc which represents the rotor thrust. For a horizontal rotor, this thrust is vertically upwards and may be used to overcome the weight of the machine to enable it to hover.

The increase in static pressure of the air in passing through the actuator disc is achieved by doing work on the air. This work is done by the engine of the helicopter. It is therefore advantageous to keep the pressure rise as small as possible. Since the rotor thrust is given by this pressure difference multiplied by the area of the disc, it is clearly important to have the rotor area as large as possible. In fact, it may be shown that the power required to generate a given amount of thrust varies approximately in inverse ratio to the rotor diameter. For example, doubling the diameter of a helicopter rotor would enable it to hover with approximately half the power. It is this very strong dependence of power on size that makes the helicopter, with its large rotor, so much more efficient in hovering flight than other kinds of vertical take-off and landing aircraft.

Another aspect of helicopter rotor performance can be established from the actuator disc model. That is the dependence of thrust and power on air density. In this case it may be shown that, again to a reasonable order of approximation, the power required to generate a given thrust varies inversely as the square root of the air density. Now the density of the air in the atmosphere is constantly changing, since it depends on both air temperature and air pressure. Just a casual observation of air pressure and temperature as recorded by a barometer and a thermometer will indicate that these change quite markedly from hour to hour and from day to day. They also both drop rapidly with height above the ground. For

25

design and performance calculations a fixed atmosphere known as the International Standard Atmosphere is used.

The International Standard Atmosphere (ISA)

The ISA represents the average atmospheric conditions in North America and Continental Europe. It is based on a prescribed variation of temperature with height. At sea level the temperature is assumed to be 15°C and it falls, for the first 11 km (36,100 ft) at a constant rate of 6.5°C per km (3,280 ft). This temperature drop and the pressure drop which accompanies it lead to an exponential fall in air density as shown in the Table below. Since the power required is dependent on the square root of the air density, this quantity is also shown. It may be seen that to hover at 5,000 m (16,400 ft) requires about 30% more power than to hover at sea level.

While the ISA is of great value for design purposes, there are clearly days and places when the sea level air is at a higher or a lower temperature. These are allowed for by using Off-Standard Atmospheres. These are constructed by adding increments or decrements to the ISA. For example, ISA+25°C represents an atmosphere with a sea-level temperature of 40°C, i.e., 15°+25°. Since the power required to hover increases as the air density reduces, and air density reduces as air temperature rises, it is the ISA plus atmospheres which are critical for helicopter operation. These are known as 'Hot-High' criteria. From Table 3.1 it can be seen that to hover at 5,000 m on an ISA+25°C day requires approximately 35% more power than to hover at sea level on a standard day. This is therefore a very significant performance criterion.

TABLE 3.1
The International Standard Atmosphere

Height above sea level (m)	Temperature (°C)	Air density (kg/m^3)	Air density $\dfrac{}{1.225}$
ISA			
0	15.00	1.225	1.000
2500	−1.25	0.957	0.884
5000	−17.50	0.736	0.775
ISA+25°			
0	40.00	1.127	0.959
2500	23.75	0.876	0.846
5000	7.50	0.671	0.740

The Rotor Blades

While the helicopter rotor may, for the purposes of analysis, sometimes be regarded as an actuator disc, it is, in reality, made up of a number of rotating blades. These blades are, in cross section, of aerofoil section shape and locally they behave like part of an aeroplane wing. The optimum shape for aerofoil sections operating at forward speeds below the speed of sound, which helicopter blades currently do, consists of the kind of shape in Figure 3.1. This has a rounded leading

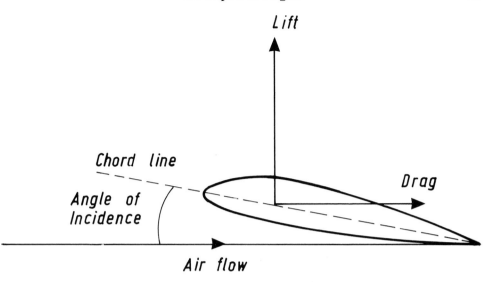

FIG. 3.1 A typical rotor blade aerofoil section

edge, a pointed trailing edge, is small in thickness in relation to the distance between the leading and the trailing edge, i.e., the chord length, and its centre line is slightly curved upwards in the centre, in other words the aerofoil section is slightly cambered.

Forces on the Aerofoil Section

When moved forward through the air, such a shape will experience a force acting on it which, to a good approximation, will vary linearly with air density and as the square of the air speed. It will also be proportional to the plan area of the section. If held at constant speed and rotated to the plan area of the section. If held at constant speed and rotated about a spanwise axis, so that the angle between the incident air flow and the chord line of the aerofoil section (known as the angle of incidence) changes, then the force will change. It is conventional to split the force produced by the motion into two components. The first is at right angles to the direction of motion and is known as the lift force. The second is directly opposed to the motion and is known as the drag force. Lift is the useful component of the force, since it supports the helicopter. Drag is the force which needs to be overcome by the engine which drives the blades: it should therefore be kept as small as possible.

The way in which the lift and drag forces vary with the incidence angle for a typical aerofoil section is shown in Figure 3.2. It can be seen that, for small angles, the lift varies linearly with incidence; above a certain angle the lift increases at a progressively smaller rate and eventually reaches a maximum. Beyond this angle, known as the stalling angle, the lift reduces with increasing incidence and the drag rises very rapidly. The stalling angle is typically between 15° and 20°; for incidences above the stalling angle, the aerofoil is said to be stalled. Also shown on the plot is the ratio of lift to drag. This shows that the optimum incidence for which the ratio of lift to drag is a maximum is well below the stalling angle.

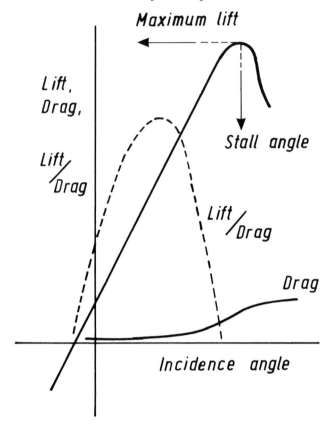

FIG. 3.2 The variation of lift and drag with incidence

Rotor Control

It has been established that the larger the rotor is for a given helicopter weight, the smaller will be the required power. There is, however, a limit on the physical size of the rotor due to the very flexible nature of the blade, which must be long and thin in order to generate adequate lift. There is also a limit on the rotor's speed of rotation. In addition, it is desirable to have the blade, in the design hovering case, operating at the incidence angle for maximum lift-to-drag ratio. These criteria, taken together, more or less dictate the design of the rotor.

To climb or descend the lift of the rotor must be varied. There are potentially two ways of doing this. One is to speed up or slow down the rotation of the blades. The other is to vary the blade angle to the airflow; that is, the incidence angle.

The first of these is never used. The main reasons are two-fold. First, the large rotor disc has a large inertia which greatly reduces the rate at which speed, and hence lift, changes may be made. Secondly, the rotor is a potent source of vibration and it generates oscillatory forces at frequencies which are multiples of the rotor rotational speed. The effects of these oscillatory forces are reduced by careful tuning of the airframe, and if the rotor speed were allowed to vary significantly this de-tuning would be impracticable.

The practical solution is to change the angle between the blade section centre-line and the plane of the rotor disc; it is called the blade pitch angle. What is required is that all the blades should change angle by the same amount. The question is: how can this be done when the blades are rotating relative to the body of the helicopter?

The solution is to use a device known as a swash plate or its equivalent. A swash plate consists of two parallel and circular plates which are separated by a bearing and can therefore rotate relative to each other. The rotating upper plate is connected to the pitch control rods of the rotor blades. The vertical position of the lower non-rotating plate is adjustable. Raising it therefore increases the pitch of all of the blades collectively and *vice versa*. The changes in blade pitch obtained are reflected in changes in the blade lift and hence in the rotor thrust; they therefore enable the hovering helicopter to climb and descend vertically. Vertical movement of the swash plate is accomplished in the cockpit by a lever – the collective pitch lever. The way in which the swash plate works is shown diagrammatically in Figure 3.3.

The increased lift associated with increased blade pitch also requires an increase in power supplied to the rotor. The engine throttle control is therefore normally incorporated into the collective lever. On modern helicopters the increased power required is supplied automatically by the engine management system. The collective lever is controlled by the pilot's left hand.

In order for the blades to change pitch, it is necessary for them to be hinged about a spanwise axis. The action of changing pitch is known as feathering and the hinge is therefore known as a feathering hinge.

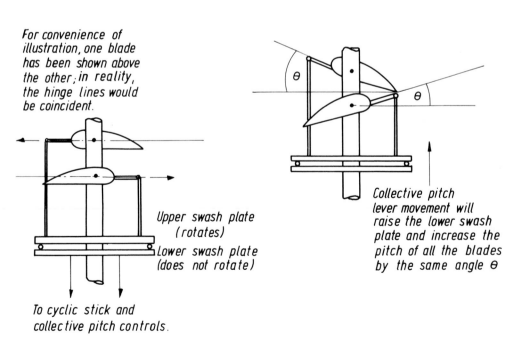

For convenience of illustration, one blade has been shown above the other; in reality, the hinge lines would be coincident.

Upper swash plate (rotates)
Lower swash plate (does not rotate)

To cyclic stick and collective pitch controls.

Collective pitch lever movement will raise the lower swash plate and increase the pitch of all the blades by the same angle θ

FIG. 3.3 Collective pitch control

FIG. 3.4 A *Gazelle* swash plate (*E. J. Everett-Heath*)

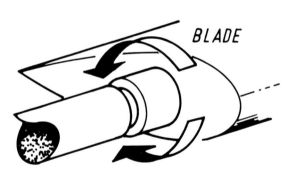

FIG. 3.5 A feathering hinge

The Tail Rotor

The power supplied to the main rotor is in the form of a torque in the main rotor drive shaft. This torque, or twisting moment, will generate a reaction in the opposite direction at the main rotor gearbox. This would cause the helicopter body to rotate in the opposite direction to the main rotor. If a helicopter has two rotors, they are made to rotate in opposite directions so that the reactive torques cancel out. For a single rotor helicopter, however, this is not possible and some other means for combating the reactive torque must be found.

FIG. 3.6 A typical tail rotor (*E. J. Everett-Heath*)

Most single rotor helicopters generate reactive torque by using a tail rotor. This works exactly like the main rotor, but is placed in a nominally vertical plane at the rear of the machine. It therefore produces a sideways thrust which, acting well behind the centre of gravity of the aircraft, also generates a torque. The tail rotor is driven directly from the main gearbox and it will rotate when the main rotor is rotating. Its thrust is controlled, like the main rotor, by varying its collective pitch and is controlled by the pilot's use of rudder pedals. He can therefore turn the helicopter body to the left or to the right about the axis of the main rotor. A typical tail rotor is depicted in Figure 3.6.

In fact, the tail rotor is something of a liability. It suffers from high drag in forward flight. It is very noisy. It is hazardous to personnel on the ground. It can easily be damaged when manoeuvring close to the ground. It requires long drive shafts and additional gearboxes. One design which overcomes some of these disadvantages is to enclose the tail rotor within the fin. As used by Aérospatiale, this is called a fenestron. It is less efficient in the hover but more efficient in forward flight.

It may be noted in passing, that if the main rotor is self-powered, for example by engines mounted on the blade tips, then the main rotor shaft carries no torque and hence there is no reactive torque to counterbalance. On such a helicopter, therefore, a tail rotor is not required.

FIG. 3.7 The *Gazelle* Fenestron (*Westland Helicopters*)

Forward Flight

Rotor Design

In forward flight, the relative airspeed across the blades on one side of the rotor disc is increased (the speed of the blades plus the speed of the aircraft) compared with the hover case; this is called the advancing side of the rotor. On the other side,

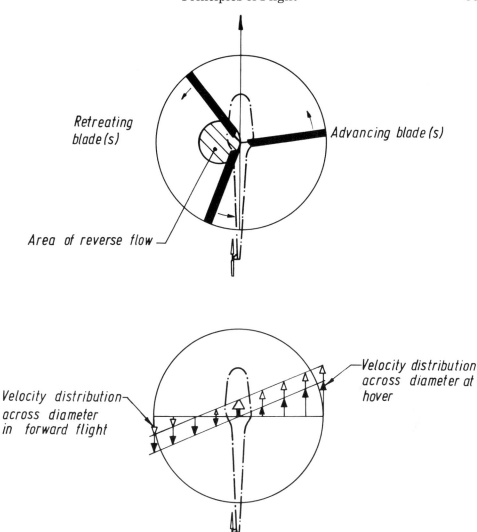

Fig. 3.8 The rotor in forward flight

the relative airspeed is reduced (the same speed of the blades minus the speed of the aircraft); this is known as the retreating side of the rotor. There is also a small area of the retreating side close to the hub where the air velocity is reversed; air travels backwards over the blades from the trailing edge to the leading edge in this reverse flow area.

Since aerodynamic lift is proportional to the square of the airspeed, a rigid rotor blade operating at constant pitch angle would generate more lift on the advancing side and less lift on the retreating side, resulting in a moment tending to roll the aircraft over. This dissymmetry in lift in forward flight may be corrected in either of two ways:

a. By varying the pitch of each blade as it rotates, reducing the pitch angle on the advancing side and increasing on the retreating side in a cyclical manner. This is cyclic pitch variation.

b. By fitting hinges at the blade root which allow the blade to flap up and down as it rotates. Because free hinges cannot transmit moments, no rolling moment can now be transmitted to the body of the helicopter. However, the resulting motion of the blades actually removes the out-of-balance moment, as was discovered by Cierva. On the advancing side, which has potentially more lift, the blade flaps up relative to its fore and aft position. This upwards motion reduces the blade local incidence and hence its lift. The opposite effect occurs on the retreating side. The lift force is thus automatically balanced on the two sides of the rotor disc by the flapping motion permitted by the flapping hinges.

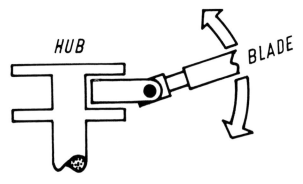

FIG. 3.9 Flapping hinges

Until recently the flapping hinge method was universally used, but advances in materials and rotor control have resulted in hingeless rotors becoming possible; these use the cyclic pitch method of equalising lift. It should be noted that hinges do not have to be pin-joints. The rotor on the *Lynx*, for example, appears to have only a feathering hinge; in fact, the flapping motion takes place by the bending of the central titanium forging which is quite shallow.

FIG. 3.10 The *Lynx* semi-rigid rotor head (*E. J. Everett-Heath*)

Flapping however produces a further problem. As a blade rotates and flaps up and down, the blade's centre of gravity will change its distance from the axis of rotation. This causes it to attempt to speed up and slow down relative to the shaft as it rotates.

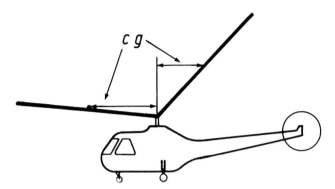

FIG. 3.11 Motion of blade centre of gravity

The rotor blade is not normally flexible enough in the plane of the rotor disc to allow this to happen and large forces are set up in the blades. These may be relieved by allowing the blades freedom to move in the drag direction by providing drag hinges. They allow the blades to lead or lag in their motion and are therefore also called lag hinges. They are frequently fitted with dampers to damp out mechanical oscillations which may otherwise cause serious problems.

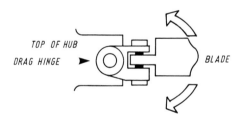

FIG. 3.12 Lag hinges

Modern hingeless rotors which eliminate the lag hinge and its associated damper permit a certain amount of lag bending, but great care must be given to the avoidance and early detection of fatigue damage. Again, on the *Lynx* rotor head, the lag hinge is not a pin-joint, but a flexible element, this time known as a dog bone because of its obvious shape; see Figure 3.10.

Rotor Control

In order to move the helicopter in any horizontal direction, it is necessary to generate a force in that direction. For example, forward flight requires a forward thrust component. This can be produced by tilting the main rotor as shown in Figure 3.13.

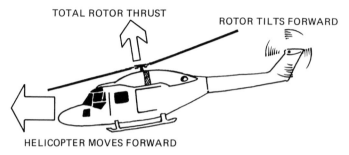

TOTAL ROTOR THRUST

ROTOR TILTS FORWARD

HELICOPTER MOVES FORWARD

FIG. 3.13 Forward transition

This tilt is achieved by altering the lift on each blade as it rotates, by cyclical variation of the blade pitch angle. This is called a cyclic pitch change and is achieved by the pilot's moving the cyclic stick fore and aft or laterally in the cockpit; see Figure 3.15. Note that lateral movement of the stick tilts the rotor sideways and is used by the pilot for lateral control.

There are several ways of changing the blade pitch cyclically but the most common is to tilt the swash plate (or its equivalent) as shown in Figure 3.14.

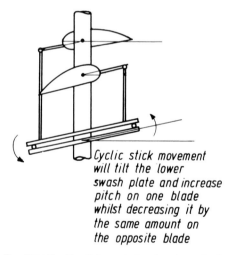

Cyclic stick movement will tilt the lower swash plate and increase pitch on one blade whilst decreasing it by the same amount on the opposite blade

FIG. 3.14 Cyclic pitch control using a swash plate

It will be recalled that the swash plate is also used to make collective pitch changes.

By putting together the effects of collective pitch, cyclic stick and tail rotor controls, it is possible to see exactly how controlled flight is achieved and what actions are needed from the pilot to maintain control. This is shown diagrammatically in Figure 3.15.

It can be seen that, for almost every manoeuvre executed by the helicopter, the pilot needs to make continual corrections with all three controls. It is for this reason that automatic systems, designed to reduce the pilot's work load, have been

FLIGHT REGIME	ACTIONS BY PILOT	EFFECTS
From ground to hover	Keeps Stick Central  — Raises Lever Balance torque with rudder pedals	Blades cone up with increased pitch 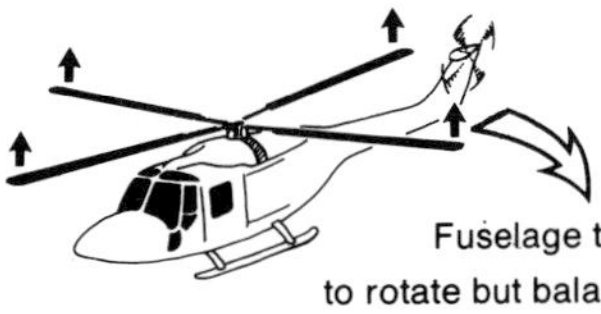 Fuselage tends to rotate but balanced by increase in tail rotor pitch
Transition from hover to forward flight	Pushes stick forward 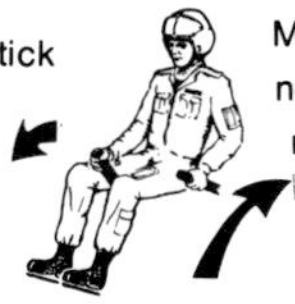 — More lift needed so raises lever further More pedal to balance increase in torque	Blades cone up further Rear blade flaps up 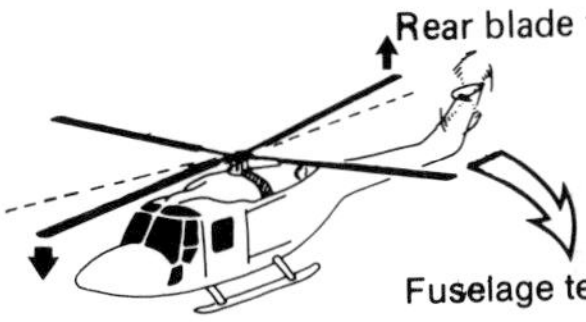 Forward blade flaps down Fuselage tends to rotate further but balanced by tail rotor
Cruise flight	Trims stick to balance datum  — Locks lever to required pitch setting Maintains balanced flight with rudder pedals	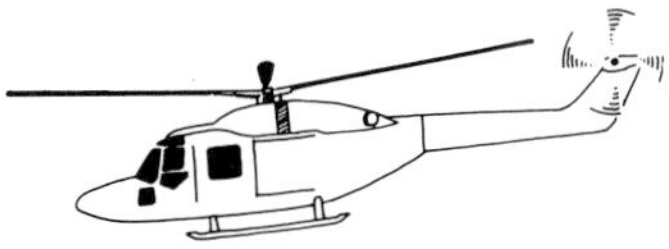 Aircraft enters balanced forward flight condition
Descending flight	Maintains forward flight 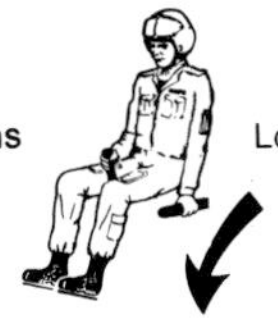 — Lowers lever Applies opposite rudder pedal to reduce anti-torque	Blades cone down Flap up  — Flap down Reduced torque causes fuselage to move in opposite direction
Spot turn in hover	Maintains hover over central spot with stick  — Slight adjustments to maintain height with lever Depresses rudder pedal in direction of turn	 Fuselage moves round axis of main hub

FIG. 3.15 How a helicopter is controlled

introduced. These systems may be classified as stability augmentation systems (SAS), or as automatic flight control systems (AFCS). They are discussed in Chapter 5.

Types of Rotor

A rotor having all three sets of hinges described previously is called a fully articulated rotor. A possible arrangement is shown in Figure 3.16.

In practice, the designer may arrange the hinges in any order. When fitted with lag dampers and other devices, it may be extremely complicated, resulting in high constructional and maintenance costs. It is also aerodynamically very 'dirty' and therefore will have a high drag.

A significant problem with a fully articulated rotor is its inability to transmit the desirable moments to the aircraft needed to control it, because the flapping hinge is fitted in order to prevent undesirable moments being transmitted in forward flight. Although there are methods of increasing control power by small amounts, this basic weakness makes a fully articulated rotor sluggish and relatively unmanoeuvrable. Manoeuvrability is highly desirable in any military aircraft but particularly in one which normally operates at low level on the battlefield.

In order to increase control moments available from the rotor, to simplify the rotor hub and to reduce its drag, the fully articulated rotor is replaced in many modern aircraft by one of the following:

a. The semi-rigid rotor which retains the feathering hinge but replaces the

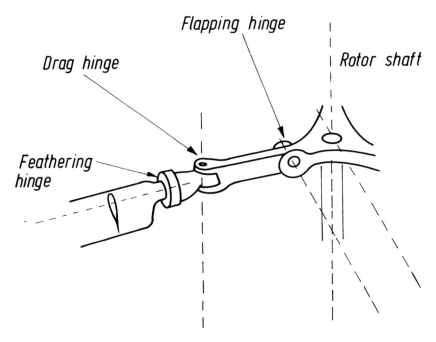

FIG. 3.16 A fully articulated rotor

flapping and lag hinges by flexible metal elements. This is the rotor system used on the *Lynx*.

b. Elastomeric bearings which replace the conventional free hinge by 'solid bearings' constructed of alternate layers of elastomeric, or rubber-like, material and metal shims. The material distorts under load and permits limited blade movement. These bearings will transmit rotor moments and will provide a certain amount of damping but are free of fatigue problems.

c. A bearingless rotor having a rotor head containing no physical hinges. All control movements are transmitted by bending parts of the rotor head.

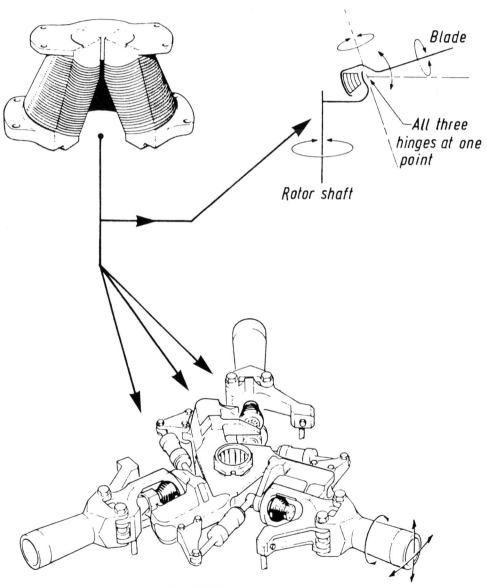

Fɪɢ. 3.17 An elastomeric rotor

The latest generation of rotors may also contain fail-safe components so that failure of any single component will not lead to total rotor failure.

Forward Flight Performance

We have already seen that, in the hover, a certain amount of power is required to maintain rotor thrust, and that this is reduced if the area of the rotor disc is increased. This is because more air is influenced in a given time and so less work needs to be done on it. The same argument can be applied to the rotor in forward flight. The faster forward that the helicopter flies, the more air the rotor influences in a given time and therefore the less the power needed to fly. This power, i.e., the power used in the generation of lift, and hence of rotor thrust, is called induced power.

The main power requirement in high speed forward flight is the power needed to overcome the drag of the helicopter body and other parts exposed to the airflow. It can be shown that the drag of these parts of the aircraft increases approximately with the square of the forward speed. It follows, therefore, that the power needed to move them through the air increases with the cube of the wind speed. This naturally rises very rapidly as the aircraft forward speed increases. The power needed to overcome these drag components is known as parasite power. There is also a certain amount of power used in driving the rotor blades round against their

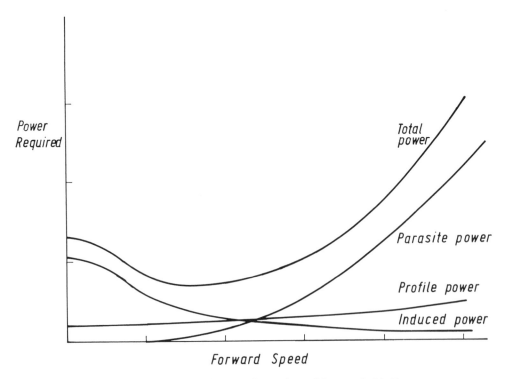

FIG. 3.18 The power required against forward speed for a typical helicopter

own drag. This increases relatively slowly with flight speed, however. It is called profile power.

The total power required for helicopter flight is therefore the sum of these three components and will look something like Figure 3.18.

It is noteworthy that the power required starts to fall as the helicopter gains speed. This phenomenon can be used to fly helicopters at weights above the maximum allowable hovering weight. This is done by the use of a rolling take-off so that the helicopter only becomes airborne when the power required has fallen below the hover requirement. It is also evident that there is a speed at which the power required is a minimum. This is the speed at which to fly if maximum endurance is sought, since, with the power being used at a minimum, the rate of fuel usage will also be minimised.

Autorotation

Should the only engine of a single-engined helicopter fail in flight, the main rotor takes on the function of the blades of an autogiro by continuing to rotate and provide lift without their being driven by the engine. However, to maintain normal rotor speed the pilot must lower the collective lever immediately to reduce the blade pitch angle and therefore the drag to the minimum. The difference between the state of autorotation and the normal flight condition is that the flow of air through the main rotor is upwards instead of downwards. This upward flow keeps the rotor turning at its normal operating speed and allows the aircraft to glide to earth. At about 30 m (100 ft) above the ground the pilot reduces his forward speed by moving the cyclic stick to the rear; this is known as flaring. Then, by levelling the fuselage and using the energy remaining in the rotor, he uses the collective lever to cushion the aircraft on to the ground, normally touching down at a low forward speed. A zero forward speed autorotative landing is possible.

A safe landing without power can therefore be made, albeit with an initially high rate of descent. In fact, it is the initial high rate of descent needed to enter controlled autorotative flight which makes hovering between about 3 m and 120 m (400 ft) and forward flight at low level potentially hazardous. If there is insufficient height available to enter steady autorotation the landing will be both heavy and uncontrolled.

It is unlikely that a twin-engined helicopter would suffer a double engine failure and be faced with an autorotative landing but, should both engines fail, the same technique would be used.

Helicopter Speed Limitations

One significant drawback to the helicopter is its limited performance in forward flight, both in absolute speed and in manoeuvrability. While for 'nap of the earth' operations the forward speed limitation may not be critical, because of the difficulties of high speed flight close to the ground, limitations on manoeuvrability impose their own constraints.

Manoeuvrability may be defined as the ability to generate lateral acceleration. In order to do this it is necessary to provide a force acting in the direction in which

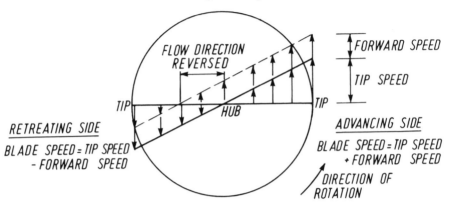

FIG. 3.19 The speed differential across a rotor

acceleration is required. The magnitude of the force needed to produce a given acceleration, and hence a given change of direction in flight, depends on the weight of the aircraft being accelerated. A useful way of comparing the manoeuvrability of vehicles of differing weights is therefore given by dividing the manoeuvring force available by the weight of the vehicle. This ratio is referred to as the load factor. Since by far the largest force available for manoeuvring a helicopter is the thrust of the main rotor, the ratio of maximum main rotor thrust to the all-up-weight is a good measure of the inherent manoeuvrability of the helicopter.

Both the forward speed and manoeuvrability limitations have the same root cause. To understand this consider Figure 3.19. This is a plan view of a helicopter rotor viewed from above. The solid line indicates the local speed of the blades in the hover. This varies from zero at the rotor hub to a maximum at the blade tips and is the same for all azimuth positions of the blade. When the helicopter moves forward however, the speed of the advancing blade, on the right hand side of the rotor disc shown, is increased, while the speed of the retreating blade on the left hand side of the disc is reduced. This is shown by the dotted line. The lift available from any section of the blade is proportional to the square of the speed, and for a single rotor helicopter, the lift on the two sides of the disc must be equal, as discussed previously. So the loss of lifting capability on the retreating side of the disc cannot be compensated by the increase in lift available on the advancing side. The maximum lift potentially available from a single helicopter rotor therefore reduces as the forward speed of the helicopter increases.

In fact, this situation becomes so bad at high forward speeds that the retreating blade, which is moving most slowly, will tend to stall. One possible way of preventing this would be to speed up the whole rotor. The problem is not solved by this, however, because another problem appears on the other side of the rotor disc. At the tip of the advancing blade, its speed relative to the air, which is the sum of the helicopter forward speed and the rotor tip speed, approaches the speed of sound. This causes, among other things, a very large drag increase and a loss of lift. The net result of all this is that there is an almost fixed optimum tip speed for all helicopters and also a severe forward speed limitation. This is illustrated in Figure 3.20.

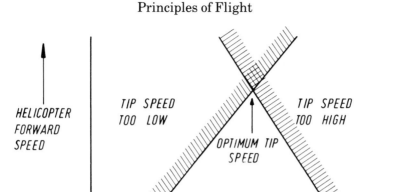

FIG. 3.20 Optimum tip speed and forward speed limitation

In fact, the maximum lift potentially available at low forward speeds cannot normally be utilised because of power limitations. The load factor achievable by a conventional helicopter then tends to increase rather slowly with increased helicopter forward speed until the speed limitations referred to above are encountered. The overall effect on the forward flight manoeuvre capability of a conventional helicopter is indicated in Figure 3.21.

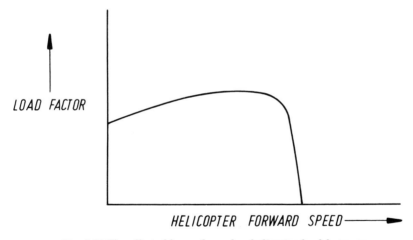

FIG. 3.21 The effect of forward speed on helicopter load factor

Types and Configurations

One way of alleviating the problem described above is to equip the helicopter with small fixed wings. These develop lift which is proportional to the square of the forward speed of the helicopter and can therefore compensate, to some extent, for the loss of rotor lift. It is not feasible to provide too much lift from a fixed wing, however, as the rotor blades need to maintain some lift to prevent them from flapping down and striking the helicopter body. The weight of the wing will reduce

FIG. 3.22 A Soviet Mi-6 *Hook* with stub wings

FIG. 3.23 The British *Rotodyne* compound helicopter (*Fairey/Westland
Helicopters*)

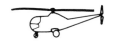

(a) Single-rotor helicopter
with tail rotor

(b) Tandem

(c) Tandem overlapping

(d) Side-by-side
non-intermeshing

(e) Co-axial contra-rotating

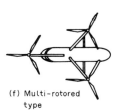

(f) Multi-rotored
type

FIG. 3.24 Possible configurations

the payload of the helicopter and it will have its own drag. Another disadvantage is that the area of the wing reduces the available rotor lift in the hover. If rolling take-offs are used, which are popular with Soviet pilots, for example, this is not serious. The wing compensates for some of these disadvantages by providing a useful mounting point for armaments.

The fixed wing, while it improves manoeuvrability in forward flight, cannot, on its own, significantly increase the maximum forward speed. Additional sources of forward thrust are needed as well. A helicopter having a fixed wing and additional thrust is known as a compound helicopter; a typical compound design is shown in Figure 3.23.

Many different helicopter configurations have been tried; six are shown in Figure 3.24. Design has tended to stabilise on the conventional main and tail rotor layout, although there are other types in service.

Helicopter aerodynamics is a complex subject which has been covered only in outline in this chapter. However, the basic fundamentals are common to all types of helicopter and must be understood if the capabilities and limitations of these machines are to be appreciated.

4.

Power Plants and Transmissions

The value of the military helicopter today is due in no small measure to its ability to carry a useful payload over a good range. For a given design, this depends on the efficiency of the engine, which should have a good power-to-weight ratio coupled with a low specific fuel consumption. Except for very small helicopters, which are no longer widely used by military forces, the gas turbine engine is used exclusively.

The Gas Turbine Engine

The earliest helicopters were fitted with reciprocating petrol engines because these were highly developed and they offered a fair power-to-weight ratio, a good specific fuel consumption, good reliability and were readily available in various sizes. As the need for increased power became evident, petrol engines became increasingly complex, multi-cylinder designs, their weight tended to increase and reliability became worse. Meanwhile, early gas turbine engines were becoming more efficient, but not yet as efficient as the best petrol engines, more reliable, and, most important of all, were able to provide very much higher power-to-weight and power-to-volume ratios. This was particularly so of the free turbine, which dispensed with the need for a clutch in the transmission system, a draw-back in all reciprocating engines. The gas turbine thus became the most important engine employed in helicopter propulsion.

Configurations

The gas turbine is also widely used in fixed-wing aircraft. In this application it is usually a turbojet or a turbofan, which generates a high-speed jet to propel the aircraft forward at high subsonic or supersonic speeds. In helicopters, however, the gas turbine is not used as a means of producing a high-velocity jet but to produce power in the form of a rotating output shaft. This is connected to the helicopter rotors through a mechanical transmission system and is known as a turboshaft engine. It is a close relation of the fourth and final variant, the turboprop, widely used on modern propeller-driven, fixed-wing aircraft.

Principles of Operation

The principal function of any engine, broadly speaking, is to convert heat into a useful form of mechanical power. No engine is capable of carrying out this conversion with an efficiency of 100%. However, engines can be built to perform at what are regarded as good efficiencies, and the gas turbine is such an engine.

It is based on a sequence of continuous operations in which different processes are successively carried out to produce useful power. The major components which constitute the heart of the gas turbine, which is called the gas generator, are shown diagrammatically in Figure 4.1 in their relative working positions.

What happens to the flow of gas when it leaves the turbine (T) determines whether the engine is a turboshaft or a turbojet.

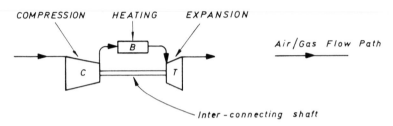

FIG. 4.1 Diagrammatic layout of a gas generator

In Operation

In operation, the turbine receives high-pressure, hot gas (a mixture of air and combustion products) which flows through the blades at high speed, causing the turbine wheel to rotate. In so doing the energy content of the gas is depleted to some extent. The energy extracted by the turbine wheel is transmitted through a rotating central shaft to the aerodynamic compressor (C) upstream, which behaves in roughly the opposite manner to the turbine, absorbing its output. The compressor draws in atmospheric air, compresses it and directs it to the combustor (B). Here the air is mixed with fuel and burned to heat it to an appropriate temperature before it is directed to the turbine. The turbine then allows the hot, high-pressure gas to expand through its blading, producing the power to drive the compressor. These three components, the compressor, the combustor and the turbine, form the gas generator. In the case of the turbojet, the partially expanded gas leaving the gas generator flows directly to the propelling nozzle, as shown in Figures 4.2 and 4.3.

This type of gas turbine produces a high-velocity jet of gas from the nozzle (N) as

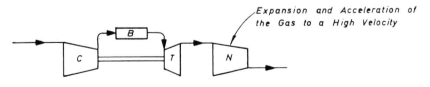

FIG. 4.2 Diagrammatic layout of a turbojet engine

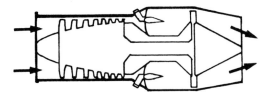

FIG. 4.3 Cross-section of a simple turbojet engine

its useful output. This output is the propulsive force. Turbojet engines have been used on compound helicopters to provide additional forward speed. However, the turboshaft engine in which we are much more interested for helicopter application is shown in Figures 4.4 and 4.5.

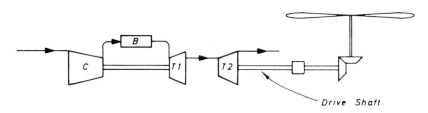

FIG. 4.4 Diagrammatic layout of a turboshaft engine

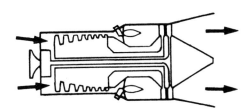

FIG. 4.5 Cross-section of a turboshaft engine

In this arrangement the gas producer, C+B+T1, behaves just as before. But immediately downstream of turbine T1 is another turbine T2. T1 and T2 are known, respectively, as the high- and the low-pressure turbines. Turbine T2, frequently mechanically separate from the gas generator section and able, there-fore, to rotate at a different speed, is now also able to provide a direct drive to the load. The gas flowing through turbine T2 gives up most of its remaining energy to the turbine.

In the case of a helicopter, the rotor is the load, being driven through a reduction gearbox. This is a typical turboshaft layout.

For completeness, variations on the two schemes described are illustrated in the cross-sections in Figures 4.6 and 4.7. The turbofan is a 'bypass' variant of the turbojet and the turboprop is a fixed-wing, shaft power unit having many similari-ties to the turboshaft engine.

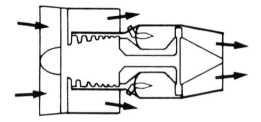

FIG. 4.6 Cross-section of a turbofan engine

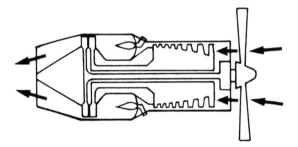

FIG. 4.7 Cross-section of a turboprop engine

Different Types of Turboshaft

There are two turboshaft configurations which are available. They are known as the free (power) turbine and the fixed turbine (or single shaft). There are several important distinctions between the two, both in their layout and application in helicopters.

The Fixed Turbine

A diagrammatic arrangement of a fixed turbine engine is shown in Figure 4.8 and a cross-section of an actual fixed turbine engine in Figure 4.9.

The most important feature of this type of engine is that the output shaft, which feeds power to the gearbox and then to the rotor through a clutch, is directly connected to the single turbine. Thus there is a fixed relationship between the rotor rotational speed and the engine rotational speed. Since a helicopter rotor runs at approximately constant speed, the consequence is that the fixed turbine engine is constrained to operate at approximately constant rotational speed also. While this

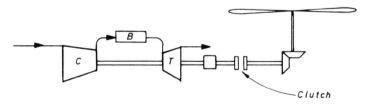

FIG. 4.8 Diagrammatic layout of a fixed turbine engine

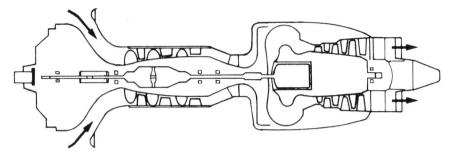

FIG. 4.9 Cross-section of a Turbomeca *Astazou* engine

arrangement offers one or two advantages, such as a very rapid response to a load change imposed by an increase in rotor collective pitch, it also results in a rather inflexible engine. For example, since it is a constant speed engine it has to be rated at a rather modest power because of the need to sustain the chosen rotational speed. There is thus a built-in power limitation which prevents the achievement of high emergency powers even for short durations. In addition, the torque-speed characteristics of the engine are not well matched to the rotor. However, this problem can be largely dealt with by the provision of a suitable engine control system. There is also a weight penalty associated with the clutch and, finally, the specific fuel consumption at low or moderate powers is poor compared with that at the maximum power condition.

The main proponents of the fixed turbine type, Turbomeca in France, have built a series of such engines over a long period. Their particular design, shown in Figure 4.9, features the output shaft emerging from the compressor, or intake, end of the engine. This contrasts with the simpler design in Figure 4.8. Apart from the mechanical design arrangements, this particular layout is no different in principle from that shown in Figure 4.8.

Free Turbine

The free turbine is the most commonly used configuration in both single-engine and multi-engine helicopters. The main reason for the widespread adoption of this type is its favourable torque-speed characteristic. It promotes rotor speed stability, reasonable specific fuel consumption at part-power operation, and the simplicity resulting from the absence of a clutch in the output drive line. A diagrammatic layout of a free turbine engine is shown in Figure 4.10, with a cross-section of an actual free turbine engine in Figure 4.11.

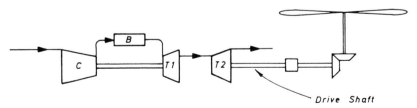

FIG. 4.10 Diagrammatic layout of a free turbine engine

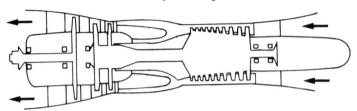

FIG. 4.11 Cross-section of a Rolls-Royce *Gnome* engine

The diagrammatic layout highlights the characteristic feature of the free turbine type, which is the absence of a mechanical connection between the gas generator (C+B+T1) and the output turbine (T2), which is thus free. In fact in a helicopter application the free turbine rotates at substantially constant speed under all conditions, apart from transient states such as start-up and run-down. It is the gas generator which is free to operate over a range of speeds, to enable its gas flow to be best matched to the requirements of the power turbine. It should be noted that the power absorbed by the rotor may vary greatly according to operating conditions, despite the fact that the rotor speed is nominally constant. Thus the freedom presented by the ability of the gas generator section to run at different speeds as required is considerable. However, the free turbine description really means no more than that the power turbine has a gas flow rather than mechanical link to the gas generator. The free turbine, therefore, behaves rather like a torque converter.

Component Detail

Apart from the distinction between the free turbine and the fixed turbine there are several other notable features which characterise certain designs.

Some engines have a wholly axial-flow compressor in which the air flows parallel to the axis of the shaft. Such a type is the Rolls-Royce *Gnome* engine, shown in Figure 4.11. It has a multi-stage compressor, and in order to obtain the desired flexible operating characteristics the first four rows of stators, which are fixed blades interspersed between the rotating compressor blades, have a mechanical arrangement to allow the blade angles to be altered. This ensures that the angle at which the flow of air meets the compressor blades is the most efficient. Such a device is a feature that would tend to be associated with first generation engines. Compression ratios of about 10:1 can be achieved by axial compressors.

An alternative approach is to adopt the Turbomeca pattern in which one or more axial-flow stages are succeeded by a centrifugal compressor which draws air in at the centre and forces it out at the outer edges by the action of the radiating vanes in a radial flow. The adoption of the centrifugal, or radial, stage tends to increase the engine cross-section, but this is not usually a serious disadvantage for a helicopter. Compression ratios of around 4:1 are common with this type of compressor.

One way of obtaining a high-pressure ratio in the compressor is to adopt a multi-shaft approach, as is done in the Rolls-Royce *Gem* engine, shown in Figure 4.12. In this free turbine engine the gas generator itself has two coaxial shafts which run

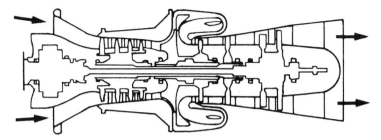

FIG. 4.12 Cross-section of a Rolls-Royce *Gem* engine

one inside the other. One is connected to the axial, and the other to the centrifugal compressor.

The four-stage, axial-flow compressor lies upstream of the centrifugal compressor and each rotates at its best speed on its own shaft. The overall high pressure rise is thus obtained while preserving good handling characteristics without having to incorporate variable stator blades.

It follows that the two-shaft, or two-spool, gas generator of the *Gem* must have a high-pressure turbine on one shaft to drive the centrifugal compressor, and a lower or intermediate pressure turbine on the other shaft to drive the axial compressor. Examination of the layout in Figure 4.12 will confirm this. These two turbines are

FIG. 4.13 The *Gem* engine (*E. J. Everett-Heath*)

the axial-flow type, which is nearly always a feature of the gas turbine engine whether turboshaft or turbojet.

Another notable feature of the *Gem* engine is the reverse-flow combustor which is well matched to the radial-flow compressor immediately upstream of it. The adoption of this feature enables the designer to shorten the whole engine and so minimise mechanical problems which sometimes arise with long shafts.

The *Gem* is fairly unusual in that, while it is of the free turbine configuration, the output drive is taken through the gas generator out of the intake end. This has certain advantages in avoiding the output shaft passing through the wall of the exhaust and, in addition, may make siting of the engine on the helicopter, in relation to the rotor, much easier.

It should be noted that an engine may incorporate a reduction gearbox. High rotational speeds of gas turbines may lead to overall reduction ratios of the order of about 100:1 in some installations. Thus a gearbox giving part of the overall reduction may be part of the engine as supplied.

Finally, the concept of modular construction is important. This technique, in which a complete engine is designed as a collection of individual modules, such as, say, a compressor module, a free turbine module, or any other module, which can be assembled relatively easily, is said to result in a reduction in operational costs. The idea is that an unserviceable engine can be quickly repaired by exchanging the bad module for a good module. Otherwise the complete unserviceable engine would be withdrawn for overhaul. In this way, good modules are retained in service and fewer spare engines are required to sustain operations.

Special Helicopter Requirements

It need hardly be mentioned that, ideally, any aero-engine should have a low acquisition cost and a low operating cost. A high thermodynamic efficiency, which also means a high fuel efficiency, is important and, of course, influences operating costs. Also desirable are high reliability and easy maintenance, both of which influence acquisition and operating costs.

However, there are several areas in which engine features special to helicopter operation are important. Perhaps the most important of these is the need for very rapid response to the pilot's demands. In particular, when a pilot requires an unforeseen power increase, say to combat adverse weather conditions on landing, he wants a rapid response from the engine. There are two sides to this requirement. Recognising that the power response characteristics of the free turbine configuration are inferior to those of the fixed turbine arrangement (because the former requires the acceleration of the whole of the gas generator section), one manufacturer at least has developed a special governor to harness the superior characteristics of the fixed-shaft engine, which is essentially a fixed-speed engine. The benefits of obtaining a power increase merely by raising turbine entry temperature, rather than by the time-consuming spinning up of the gas generator to increase the gas through-flow, are substantial. It is interesting to note that the Rolls-Royce *Gem* engine features a different approach to the problem of obtaining rapid response. The gas generator section of this free turbine engine consists of two spools which have contributed to the good response characteristics without going to the complication of variable stators.

Perhaps the second most important requirement is good part-load fuel economy. This is particularly so in the twin-engined helicopter whose engine size is designed to be able to meet an engine-out requirement. The consequence is that under normal cruising conditions each engine is operating at about 50% of its maximum rating. The gas turbine tends to be poor at part-loads, and so an engine required for such an application would tend to be designed for a high pressure ratio and maximum cycle temperature that would afford a reasonable part-load economy. These features could result in adverse handling characteristics. However, it is true that the part-load fuel economy of the free turbine engine is superior to that of the fixed turbine engine, so multi-engine helicopters invariably use the free turbine type.

In addition to those important features already mentioned, there is also the need to be able to cope with intake air which has been contaminated by dirt or sand or exhaust gas. Depending on the siting of the engine(s) in relation to the main rotor gearbox, the intake air flow may be significantly disturbed. The ability to operate on contaminated fuel as well as on a range of fuels is also important. Finally, the vibration environment presented in helicopter operation is arduous and the structure of the engine thus needs to be very stiff.

The Transmission

The primary function of the transmission system is to transmit the drive provided by the engine to the rotor. In a single rotor helicopter there is a secondary function of providing drive to the anti-torque tail rotor.

It was noted before that some helicopter engines have an integral reduction gearbox. This means that a more manageable order of output in terms of revolutions per minute is provided. In all cases this rotational speed is much greater than the rotor requires and so further speed reducing must be provided. Furthermore, since most engines are positioned in the fuselage at right angles to the rotor mast, the transmission must turn the drive through this right angle. This dual function is accomplished in a bevel-type reduction gearbox.

Twin-engined helicopters need a gearbox which will accept two input drives to provide a single main output drive. This is a complex arrangement in which the power output of the two engines must be carefully matched. Such an installation is that in the *Puma* helicopter. The two Turbomeca *Turbo* engines provide the input at 23,000 rpm, while the single output to the rotor is reduced to 265 rpm. This is an overall reduction ratio of about 100:1 which is not easily accomplished.

Quite apart from providing the proper speed reduction, the main gearbox and ancillaries should ideally be as light as possible, transmitting little vibration to the fuselage and offering reliable performance with a respectable overhaul time. Transmissions today are highly developed, much progress having been made since the days of the widespread use of the reciprocating engine. This has been achieved by raising allowable stress levels in gearing through better design and the use of better materials and manufacturing techniques. An advanced design of gearbox is that in the Westland WG30 helicopter. It is a shallow, low-maintenance, conformal design and is mounted on a vibration-absorbing raft along with two *Gem* engines, the whole raft itself being mounted on elastomeric suspension units. In this way, vibration is absorbed by the raft instead of being transmitted to the fuselage.

Future Technology

Priorities

Engine manufacturers continually striving to improve their product naturally concentrate on those aspects that require most attention. All aspects of engine performance can be improved, but the manufacturer has to balance, for example, the development time and cost against the improvement in, say fuel consumption, or reduction in weight, or perhaps improved reliability. In the following paragraphs examples of technological improvements which are likely to be important in the next ten years or so are mentioned.

Reliability

One of the most significant areas requiring attention is that of reliability. All operators require the engine to perform as predicted and unscheduled interruptions are both inconvenient and costly. It may well be that a reduced emphasis on improved pure performance, such as increased turbine entry temperature, component efficiency or reduced engine weight, could be more than offset, in terms of cost of operation, by increasing the emphasis on improved component and system reliability and relatively unsophisticated engine features. This approach is not intended to inhibit the introduction of improved technological features, but is suggested as a means of pacing the introduction of innovations.

Improving Specific Fuel Consumption

Reliability is such an all-embracing aspect that it is almost impossible to mention other considerations which do not influence it. However, another requirement which will probably continue to challenge the engine manufacturer is the improvement of specific fuel consumption, particularly at cruise conditions when the twin-engined machine is running at a low percentage power. It may be that more highly optimised engine cycles will be adopted. A possible development for a long-range or long-endurance application is a recuperative engine similar to the *Abrams* tank engine. Such advances that do occur will have to take place while maintaining good handling qualities. Improvements in engine fuel management systems, mentioned in Chapter 5, will lead to improved response times, particularly in the free turbine engine.

Engine Intake Protection

The helicopter frequently operates in a hostile environment in the sense that the engine ingests foreign matter such as dust, stones and ice. Separating out such material and/or filtering pre-intake air are problems particular to the military helicopter. Engine intake protection in the form of particle separators may well be a standard feature in due course.

Infra-red Suppression

For some years the suppression of infra-red radiation from exhaust systems and exhaust gas has been actively pursued. Several measures have been used and these are described in Chapter 7.

Reduction of Weight

The application of composite materials is now quite common. It seems certain that their light weight and low cost will ensure their increasing use, particularly where high temperatures do not occur. In engines, in particular, ceramics show promise; however, it may be more than ten years hence before a production engine is available.

Reduction of Cost

Finally, in these days of strictly controlled budgets, perhaps the most important considerations of all are the costs of acquiring and operating helicopter engines. Of course, the various technological points mentioned in the preceding paragraphs affect both costs. But since the operating cost for a normal life will exceed the cost of acquisition, it is thought that henceforth the manufacturer and the operator will concentrate on developments such as improved reliability, maintainability, fuel control systems and environmental protection.

FIG. 4.14 The RTM-322 (E. J. Everett-Heath)

Improved performance in terms of reliability, cruise fuel-consumption, power-to-weight ratio, handling and operating cost will assume increasing importance.

RTM-322

The Rolls-Royce/Turbomeca RTM-322 is a new family of small engines which incorporates many of the above improvements. Turboshaft, turboprop and turbofan derivatives will be based on a common engine core. The turboshaft version has a rating of 2,100 shp with a growth potential to 3,000 shp. It is a two-shaft design with a single spool power turbine, has full authority digital electronic control (explained in Chapter 5) and an electronic health and usage monitor. The RTM-322 has only 3,000 parts and six modules, including a particle separator. It is sized to power single-engined helicopters in the 4,000–6,000 kg (8,820–13,230 lb) class, twins in the 6,000–12,000 kg (13,230–26,460 lb) class and three-engined helicopters, such as the EH-101, in the 12,000–16,000 kg (26,460–35,280 lb) class.

5.

Avionics

The word avionics stems from a combination of 'aviation' and 'electronics' and signifies the use of electrical or electronic devices and systems in aircraft. This general term covers the wide and expanding range of functions in all areas of aviation. The helicopter employs technologies which are equally applicable to fixed-wing, lighter-than-air and surface-effect machines.

The Associated Technologies

At the heart of every avionics system lie all of the conventional and electronic technological developments. However, there are two fields in which these have provided capabilities which are largely specific to aircraft in every form. They are the gyroscope and the databus.

Gyroscopes

In the earliest days of aviation it was discovered that the sensory system of the pilot was inadequate when faced with his need to determine his aircraft's attitude while his view of the outside world was obscured by cloud. Not only could he not see the ground or horizon, but the influence of his inner ear balancing mechanism and his deep muscle weight sense could be confused by manoeuvring the aircraft to apply centrifugal and other acceleration forces in a direction other than that of natural gravity. In similar circumstances the gyroscope, in gimballed mountings, will automatically maintain its position in space, and when a suitable means of measuring the position of the aircraft relative to the gyro has been provided, can indicate aircraft attitude with reference to the hidden outside world.

The tendency of the gyroscope to remain in its plane of rotation is known as its rigidity or gyroscopic inertia, one of its two fundamental characteristics. The second of these is precession, where the result of any force applied to the periphery of the gyroscope wheel produces a response 90° further round its rim in the direction of rotation from the force.

Until relatively recently gyroscopes were air driven, but most, if not all, are now electrically powered, allowing smaller, lighter, and more accurate systems to be installed. These now form the basis of all flight instruments which measure aircraft attitude and direction or rate of change of either. They are also at the core of all autostabilisation or autopilot systems. However, the ring laser gyro, which detects attitude or attitude change by measuring any movement-generated distortion in a triangular field of laser light, seems likely to displace the rotating gyro in some, if not all, forms in the future.

The Databus

The increasing size and complexity of aircraft has been accompanied by the need to control, measure and display a large quantity of data from a variety of systems. Were each sensor and indicator or switch to be directly linked by a pair of dedicated wires, a modern aircraft would be festooned with electrical cable, much of which would not be in use for much of the time.

The databus removes the need for the multitude of wires by providing a highway, consisting of a much smaller number of electrical cables, to which all selectors and sensors are connected. The digital output from each sensor or selector is coded, packaged and addressed so that the relevant destination can recognise it; it is then transmitted down one or more free lanes in the databus in parallel with other sensor signals. As gaps exist between each package of data, messages from other systems can be interleaved so that delays in data transmission are avoided. The sharing of a common data path by several independent signals is known as multiplexing.

Electrical cabling is not the most efficient type of databus, because the amount of data that can be passed is limited. The fibre optic cable has a far better transmission performance and is beginning to feature prominently in current designs of high volume databusses, now that problems in providing reliable junctions with the sensors have been resolved.

Flight Control Systems

The Flying Controls

The function of the individual flying controls based on a suitable form of mechanical linkage between cyclic, collective or tail rotor pedals and the relevant blade-pitch change actuators was explained in Chapter 3. Indeed, until recently such a system was standard on every helicopter. The development of fly-by-wire technology now allows this linkage to be replaced by dedicated electrical cable linking control and actuator, or by the databus which carries the pilot control signals to the actuator using the multiplexed coding system. In either event the substitution of electrical signalling, as it is sometimes described, for the mechanical linkage, saves weight and, if a number of separate data paths are provided, can improve battlefield damage tolerance. However, such a system does become sensitive to the influence of electromagnetic interference and its design must incorporate sufficient screening to ensure safe operation in the most hostile electrical climate that the aircraft is likely to occupy.

The Stabilisation System

Unlike most fixed-wing aircraft, the helicopter is dynamically unstable in both pitch and roll in that any disturbance about these two axes will result in a tendency for the aircraft to move away from its original state or attitude, unless the pilot intervenes. This generates additional pilot workload in direct proportion to the amount of manoeuvring which the pilot is carrying out, or to turbulence which the aircraft encounters. It is caused by a fundamental aerodynamic deficiency in the aircraft. The pilot workload implications are large and can be overcome only by providing him with artificial and uncommanded assistance to remove some or all of the undesired motion.

This can be done by mounting in the aircraft a gyroscope system capable of measuring aircraft attitude or rate of change of attitude about all three axes. When a displacement is sensed by the gyro, an electrical signal measuring this movement is passed to a flight control system computer. This determines the amount of control movement needed to counter the displacement and sends the appropriate signal to the flight control actuator.

Where the measurement of attitude change is based on a rate gyro, only rate of attitude change information is generated and the computer will aim to return the aircraft to its original zero rate of change of attitude. This is known as rate stabilisation and it will be appreciated that, following a disturbance, the final aircraft attitude will eventually be different from the original. It will also be evident that this system will not hold a given attitude for long. It is a simple and relatively cheap system used mainly on the smaller, less sophisticated helicopters.

Where the direct measurement of attitude or position can be made, as with a vertical gyro measuring pitch and roll, then a signal indicating both the precise change in attitude and its rate of change can be provided, allowing not only rate stabilisation but also an automatic return to the original attitude selected by the pilot. This is known as attitude stabilisation and is the standard currently favoured for general helicopter use both in civil and military operations. It does provide a good long-term datum holding facility.

The Auto-pilot

An aircraft fitted with a stabilisation system can also carry an auto-pilot, with which to hold any appropriate data, e.g., height, heading, speed, or angle of bank. This is achieved merely by establishing the aircraft at the condition to be maintained, engaging the relevant auto-pilot function by pressing a height-hold button or removing foot pressure from the tail rotor control pedals, for example, and the aircraft will then maintain that position until directed otherwise. If an error is detected it is measured, a signal passed to the flight control computer and a correction applied to the relevant actuator, in parallel with any attitude or rate stabilisation activity that may also be taking place.

This traditional auto-pilot capability can be expanded in its helicopter employment to include an automatic hover control and an entirely automatic transition to and from the hover. The former employs either a Doppler signal or, in the case of a sonar-carrying helicopter, a cable angle sensor which is used by the flight control system to pass correction signals needed to maintain either zero Doppler speed, an absolutely vertical cable or any other value which has been set by the pilot.

The automatic transition to and from the hover uses a pre-programmed height and speed time schedule to determine what height and speed the helicopter should

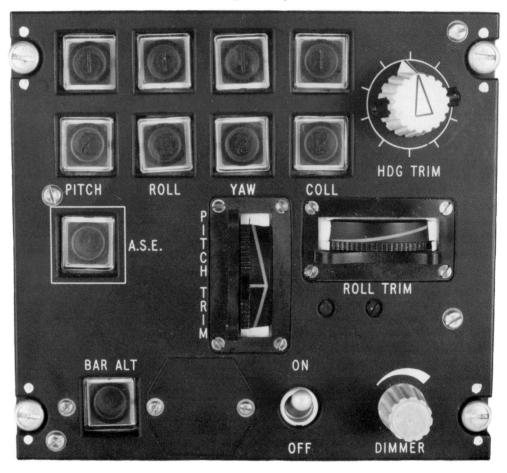

FIG. 5.1 AFCS trimmers in an Army *Lynx* (*P. G. Harrison*)

have attained at a particular point in the transition. By setting the helicopter at a particular 'gate', which could involve flying into wind at 60 m (200 ft) above the surface at 110 kph (68 mph) air speed, the selection of automatic 'transition down' will generate a progressive speed and height reduction according to the time schedule which will bring the aircraft to the hover at 12 m (40 ft) above the surface, with no pilot input. A similar system can be provided for the transition to forward flight. Both are particularly valuable in conditions of high pilot workload and hostile conditions, when the absence of vertical obstructions above the hover surface can be guaranteed. As a result this auto-pilot mode is confined to naval or SAR operations.

Power Plant Controls

A relatively new area of avionic development is the application of digital electronic fuel control to the helicopter's engine. As has already been explained, the modern turboshaft engine is a complex mechanism, with the power turbine driving to the gearbox through one shaft, inside a second, joining low pressure turbine to low pressure compressor, inside a third shaft, joining high pressure turbine to high pressure compressor. All of these components, together with ambient conditions, have an influence on engine efficiency and response. Only since the arrival of digital microelectronics has there been a facility to measure the performance of each component, analyse the result, then provide an accurate real-time calculation of the correct fuel supply needed by the engine to achieve optimum efficiency. The full authority digital engine control (FADEC) system is beginning to make a substantial impact upon the helicopter market, very much following the example of the commercial and military fixed-wing aircraft fleet.

Flight Instruments

As has already been explained, the early aviators relied upon visual cues and their own sense of balance and attitude to fly safely and successfully clear of cloud. In cloud these senses were not only largely useless, they often generated entirely erroneous balance and attitude cues which conflicted with unbiased information provided by instruments. Gyroscopic instruments were developed to provide attitude and manoeuvre information to join the simple pressure-operated instruments already provided for the measurement of air speed, height, rate of change of height and the magnetic compass.

Fig. 5.2 An Army *Lynx* instrument panel (*Westland Helicopters*)

Pressure-operated Instruments

The simplest of all flight instruments are the three which indicate various combinations of static and dynamic pressure, the air speed indicator (ASI), the altimeter and the vertical speed indicator (VSI). All are supplied with air from the pitot-static system which passes air from both the pressure head situated at the front of the aircraft and pressure vents further aft on the airframe to the relevant instrument cases.

The Air Speed Indicator

The ASI measures and displays the speed of the helicopter relative to the air around it. It consists of an airtight case divided into two parts by a flexible diaphragm. One chamber is connected to the pressure head from where it is supplied with air influenced by both static and dynamic pressure. The other chamber is supplied with air from the static vents. At rest equal pressure in both chambers causes the diaphragm to be at rest. In flight the dynamic overpressure on one side causes the diaphragm to distend accordingly, a movement which can then be fed to a calibrated instrument to present these data as air speed.

The Altimeter

The pressure altimeter is simply an aneroid barometer which measures atmospheric pressure. In a basic altimeter an airtight case containing a partially evacuated aneroid capsule is connected to the static pressure system. A leaf spring prevents the capsule from collapsing under the pressure of the surrounding air. As the aircraft climbs or descends, the change in pressure around the capsule causes it to expand or contract. This movement can then be transmitted to the face of an instrument to indicate the height above whichever datum the pilot chooses. He can set this datum using a baroscale, so that actual height above a surface can be displayed or, alternatively, the altitude above an imaginary pressure datum.

The Vertical Speed Indicator

The VSI displays rate of change of altitude in either the climb or the descent. It is a sensitive instrument, more so than the altimeter and is particularly valuable when precise control is needed during movement from one height or altitude to another, such as during a landing approach in cloud. It consists of a sensitive metal

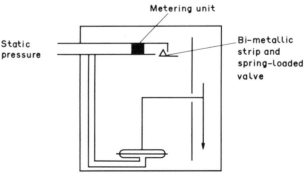

FIG. 5.3 A simple VSI

capsule inside an airtight case. The case of the instrument is fed with static pressure which flows through a metering unit, restricting the flow of air. The capsule is supplied with a free flow of static pressure. As the aircraft changes height, so disparity occurs between the current static pressure in the capsule and the immediate past pressure, which still prevails in the instrument case. The differential will vary with the rate of height change and is displayed on the face of the instrument as a vertical speed in units of height per minute. Since both temperature and pressure can influence the accuracy of this speed, the instrument contains an automatic compensation device for both variables. A simple diagram showing the layout of a VSI is shown at Figure 5.3.

Instruments Based on Gyroscopes

ATTITUDE INDICATOR

The attitude indicator, or artificial horizon as it has been described in the past, uses a horizontally-mounted gyroscope to present an indication of the aircraft's current pitch and roll attitude. It does so by mounting the instrument case, together with its markings, rigidly on the airframe and by operating the gyroscope within that case. The gyroscope uses its rigidity to remain in a constant position in space, while the aircraft, the instrument case and the marking move around it, indicating aircraft attitude. Any type of gyro can be used for this task, with electrically-driven versions being widely used. In the most modern types, the information can be generated by a central multi-purpose gyroscope and displayed remotely on a cathode ray tube (CRT). The reduction in space needed by an electrically-driven gyroscope or by the CRT display allows much additional information, mainly associated with navigation, to be shown on this type of instrument. In this form it is known as a flight director, an example of which is shown at Figure 5.4.

TURN AND SLIP INDICATOR

The turn and slip indicator displays movement of the aircraft in the yawing (i.e., movement to left and right about the vertical axis) and the rolling plane. In its simplest form it consists of two separate instruments in one case. The turn indicator employs the precession of a rate gyroscope to indicate a rate of turn. In the diagram at Figure 5.5, if the base of the gyroscope turns in the direction of the arrow as the aircraft turns to the left, the force is applied in the direction of arrow A. Precession causes the force to act at 90° in the direction of rotation, which means that the response would be seen at the point and in the direction of arrow B. This causes the pointer to move to the left on the scale, to measure the rate of the precessing force and thus the rate of turn. In modern instruments the rate of turn pointer is incorporated in the attitude indicator or flight director display.

The slip indicator merely measures the sideways movement of the aircraft along the lateral axis. A simple 'bubble' or 'ball in tube' inclonometer is mounted so that the bubble or ball is in the centre of its display when the aircraft is either level and stationary or flying precisely straight ahead. In forward flight if the pilot now yaws

FIG. 5.4 A flight director

the aircraft so that it sideslips, it acquires a sideways velocity and the lateral force acting on the bubble or ball, displaces it in the direction of the force. Conversely if the pilot uses his tail rotor control pedals to keep the bubble or ball precisely in the central position in forward flight, the aircraft will have no lateral velocity.

DIRECTION INDICATOR

The direction indicator uses a horizontally-mounted gyroscope to provide a stable reference in azimuth for accurate course steering and precise turning manoeuvres. In early versions it was manually set and updated by reference to a magnetic compass. Current instruments are fed data automatically from a magnetic reference so that the display provides an accurate indication of aircraft heading related to magnetic or true north as selected by the pilot. In this form it is known as a gyro-magnetic compass. Modern instruments invariably utilise elec-

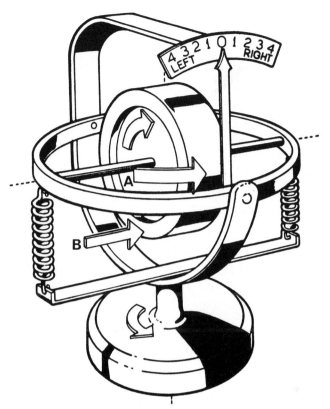

FIG. 5.5 A rate gyroscope used in a turn indicator

trically driven gyros, with the benefit that small gyro size allows a variety of additional information from remote navigation sensors to be displayed. These versions can be known as radio magnetic indicators (RMI) or horizontal situation indicators (HSI). CRT-based instruments using a central multi-purpose gyroscope system and remote navigation information are now becoming available for use in helicopters. Figure 5.6 shows a typical gyro-magnetic compass used in current military helicopters.

Communications

The commercial and military value of the helicopter is largely dependent on its efficiency as a communications platform. Not only must it carry the radio facilities needed to allow it to operate safely in airspace controlled by the civil aviation and military authorities, but it must also be capable of carrying the communications equipment specific to its role. However, problems exist in finding suitable antennae bases at appropriate points on the structure to allow satisfactory transmission and reception. The smaller the helicopter the greater becomes this problem. Difficulty can also be experienced with some types of high power radio equipment, such as high frequency transmitters, which can induce random

Fig. 5.6 A direction indicator

electrical signals in other electrical circuits within the aircraft. Where these circuits are associated with flight or engine-control systems, fundamental aircraft safety issues are raised which can often substantially influence system design, operating procedures, and permitted performance.

Radios

VERY HIGH FREQUENCY (AMPLITUDE MODULATED)

The VHF (AM) radio is carried in every helicopter which is required to communicate with civil aviation authorities. All civil and military aircraft carry this equipment.

ULTRA HIGH FREQUENCY

Every helicopter which has to communicate with military aviation authorities should carry this equipment. It is an essential part of every military helicopter's avionic installation and is also fitted to some civil aircraft.

VERY HIGH FREQUENCY (FREQUENCY MODULATED)

The VHF (FM) radio is specific to military users, where the helicopter needs a communication link with non-aviation military units. It is an essential part of the

communications system fitted to Royal Navy and Royal Marine aircraft supporting Royal Marine units, Army Air Corps aircraft supporting the Army and Royal
Air Force aircraft supporting the ground elements of all three services.

HIGH FREQUENCY

The HF radio is fitted mainly to aircraft needing a long-range voice or morse
capability. It is widely used in long range SAR operations by both the Royal Navy
and the Royal Air Force and is fitted to aircraft operating across long distances in
maritime, desert, jungle and mountainous environments. It is normally associated
with very large antennae, usually wire aerials running from tail fin to fuselage
and suspended from mountings on each side of the tail boom.

CENTRAL COMMUNICATIONS SYSTEM (CCS)

The CCS is the central control system through which the pilot selects and
controls the radio facilities of the aircraft. It provides him first with a primary and
a secondary intercommunications system between each member of the crew and
those passengers with a CCS control box at their seating position. It also contains
the switching and volume controls to allow individual radio signals to be switched
to these positions. A separate selector on each CCS control box allows the crew to
choose on which radio they will broadcast when they press the transmit button on
the relevant control.

Identification Friend or Foe

The IFF system is a means of identifying the status of an aircraft to a radar
transmitter that is scanning the area for potential targets. The radar transmits on
a specific frequency to a second transmitter carried in the aircraft which has
produced a radar return. The incoming signal triggers a transmission from the
aircraft IFF, which is coded according to a four-figure number set by the crew on
the IFF controller in the cockpit. If this code, more easily understood perhaps as a
numerical password, identifies the aircraft as friendly, then that radar return can
be ignored by the operator.

The numerical code may be changed regularly to avoid compromise and as long
as all friendly aircraft and surveillance radar operators are using the correct codes
and changing at the same time, no problems should occur. However, selection of
the incorrect code or perhaps the blanking of antennae caused by aircraft
manoeuvres at the time of the IFF challenge can result in friendly aircraft being
classified as hostile and engaged by air defence weapons.

Navigation

Doppler Driven

The Doppler effect has been described fully in Volume 8. In a helicopter
navigation system the ground speed of the machine is deduced by directing a

narrow beam of energy to the ground ahead and measuring the frequency difference between the transmitted wave and the reflected wave. The differences are independent of the distance to the reflecting surface, so height above ground and rough terrain do not effect the accuracy of the system. In a similar way drift can be deduced.

One to four beams can be used to measure speed and drift in what is commonly called the JANUS system, from the two-faced Roman god who was able to look forwards and backwards simultaneously.

The Decca tactical air navigation system (TANS), which is installed in the Westland *Lynx* and other helicopters, consists of a computer which is fed by a Doppler radar, compass, vertical reference gyroscope and true air speed (TAS) sensor. The function of the TAS sensor is to act as a back-up should the Doppler radar fail.

From the information it receives, the computer can calculate 14 different functions, of which the most important are present position in grid or latitude and longitude, and position plus bearing and distance to any one of ten different points. Heading and range to intercept any targets moving on a fixed course and speed which have been fed into the computer, called a moving way-point, can also be computed. This function is more important to the naval variant of *Lynx*. Aircrew access is through a keyboard and information in the computer can be displayed in alphanumeric form on an indicator in the unit, or a further output can drive a moving cursor on a roller map with a degree of accuracy of some 2% of distance flown, or better. The computer display shown in Figure 5.7, part of the Racal navigation system RNS 252, presents Doppler and other navigation system data to the crew.

In other aircraft systems the Doppler can provide the correction data needed by the automatic flight control system (AFCS) or auto-pilot, if an automatic hovering system using Doppler signals is installed. In maritime operations this facility will use the sea surface rather than the sea bed as its reflecting surface, with the result that the aircraft may maintain a hover relative to a surface influenced by current or tidal flow, rather than a fixed point.

While Doppler systems are not passive, the beams are directional and are directed downwards at angles of 60° or more to the horizontal. At the heights at which military helicopters are expected to fly, there is little danger of interception by the enemy, other than during very steep turns or in the rare event of overflying the appropriate sensor. However Doppler systems are susceptible to jamming.

Inertial Navigation System (INS)

The INS uses an aircraft-mounted, gyroscopically-stabilised reference from which to take very accurate measurements of aircraft motion. The aircraft motion along all three axes is sensed by the gyroscopes and measured by the acceler-ometers and then passed to a computer and processed to give velocity vector data. If the reference platform has been correctly aligned at the point of departure, its position, and thus that of the aircraft, can be accurately determined at any stage of flight. It is to this type of system, where accuracy and reliability are of great importance, that the ring laser gyro is currently being directed.

FIG. 5.7 The RNS 252 (*Racal Avionics*)

Surveillance

In the early military helicopters surveillance was carried out by using some form of direct view optical sight or binoculars. As the need for longer range or more covert surveillance developed, the need for electro-optical, thermal-sensing or radar surveillance devices became more pronounced. The electro-optical sight is particularly suited to installation on points remote from the helicopter crew, such as above the rotor head. If access can be provided via a non-rotating component of the rotor mast, electrical power can be fed to, and the digital signals taken from a television camera or from a thermal sensing/imaging camera, which can then be processed and displayed to the crew. Similar systems can be nose-mounted or roof-mounted. In both cases the simplicity inherent in providing electrical power supplies to, and the data path from the sensors to the crew is self-evident.

Radar

Radar for both maritime and battlefield surveillance is becoming more widely used as the radar, its associated equipment and power supplies come within the weight, space and power capabilities of the helicopter. Radar has been installed in a wide variety of anti-submarine helicopters for many years, the Westland *Sea*

FIG. 5.8 The dorsal radome houses the antenna for the *Sea Searcher* radar
(*Westland Helicopters*)

King Mk 5 being an example of the mounting used until recent years to provide a
near 360° coverage. The *Lynx* Mk 3 employs a nose-mounted *Seaspray* radar for
navigation, surveillance and target acquisition, albeit with the limitation that
radar coverage is limited to some 90° either side of the aircraft centre line.

The airborne early warning radar also finds a home on maritime helicopters.
The 360°-scan *Searchwater* radar that is boom-mounted on a few modified *Sea King*
Mk 2 is an example. To provide the radar with a clear 360° field of view, the
antenna is hinged to allow it to extend beneath the aircraft in flight. It is retracted
before landing.

The problems of all-round coverage present the designer of a battlefield surveillance radar installation with similar problems. The relatively small targets for the
radar, tanks, armoured personnel carriers and the like demand a large antenna to
achieve acceptable detection success rates. A hinged rotating aerial, such as the
Orchidée radar fitted to the Aérospatiale *Puma*, is currently the only means of
achieving the necessary performance.

While each type of radar offers the designer the benefits of all-weather surveillance or target acquisition, the installation has the potential to interfere substantially with other avionics systems. The need to obtain long detection ranges from
each radar, without the ability to increase substantially the antenna size, leads to
increases in the power of the radar signal. As the transmitted power increases,

FIG. 5.9 The *Searchwater* radar (*Westland Helicopters*)

there is more opportunity to cause interference or, at worst, uncommanded signals in other electrical circuits. This is particularly serious when an electronic flight control system or an electrically-operated weapon system is also fitted. Considerable design and development effort is then needed to ensure that the radar is correctly integrated into the avionics system of the helicopter.

Weapons

Helicopter avionics systems have been made substantially more complex by the installation of weapons on aircraft. Having begun as very simple electrical power and firing circuits for the remote firing of guns or rockets, avionic circuits can now carry sophisticated electro-optical, thermal-sensing or imaging and radar signals to detect and automatically track targets. Weapon system effectiveness is tied closely to the serviceability and efficiency of the system's electronics package.

While ensuring the availability of an adequate, stable power supply is a fairly simple design task, the provision of a satisfactory level of integrity in the firing circuits is more difficult. Not only has the system to cope with the problem of random electrical signals caused by communications or radar systems installed in the aircraft, but it must be protected against the influence of high power signals from transmitters that may be operating close by. A ship's radar, operating at very high power over a helicopter deck, could induce spurious signals in an unprotected electrical circuit within the aircraft.

Screening systems or protection devices must be incorporated into the weapon systems electronic package to ensure that weapons are launched and fired only when the correct firing signal is initiated by the crew.

Flight Management Systems

The proliferation of information available outside and within the helicopter has produced a steady increase in crew workload, to the point where in some cases supply exceeds processing capability. In these circumstances many data are given to the crew on facilities, aircraft systems and tactical situations that identify satisfactory operation. This distracts them from the task of operating the helicopter to the limits of its performance, in the face of a threat. Thus the separation of data into those essential to the current activity and those which are not is of some importance.

The flight management system, in one of a wide variety of forms, can offload routine tasks (such as monitoring engine conditions, fuel state and protection facilities) from the crew and present them with a warning if a failure has occurred or is about to. It can also integrate data from a variety of sensors to give a processed picture of navigation, communication, surveillance or weapon systems states.

The computer programmes needed for such a system would normally form part of the permanent memory, although provision can be made for the loading of up-to-date tactical, communications, or weapons data via a keyboard, a hand-held loading device programmed by operations staff, or a data-transfer cable plugged into the aircraft.

The display of this volume of information is largely beyond the capabilities of traditional mechanical or electronic instruments and has resulted in the development of a CRT-based multi-function display (MFD). The MFD is capable of displaying data from the flight management computer either as selected by the crew or as programmed into the memory. Thus the pilot can use one of a series of

FIG. 5.10 A modern MFD (*Smiths Industries*)

buttons or a selected point on the touch screen matrix of an MFD and the information selected will appear automatically on the screen. Each button or matrix point will have a number of functions which will appear sequentially as the selector button is pressed. Alternatively, if systems failure is imminent or has occurred, the MFD can be programmed to clear all or part of the screen to display emergency drills or procedures to advise the crew. Such is the importance of this feature of MFD capability that aircraft are invariably fitted with at least two displays, so that the failure of one CRT will not compromise the safe operation of the helicopter.

Anti-icing Systems

The operation of the military helicopter in a wide variety of weather conditions has led to the development of electrical and electronic systems to remove ice from the rotor blades, engine intakes and windscreens. Ice accretion on these components can dramatically reduce performance, cause damage to engines and block the crew's view of the outside world.

In each case the removal of ice necessitates the use of electrical power to heat the surface. In the case of windscreens, power is applied to a network of filaments embedded in the screen, heat being applied whenever the temperature of the screen drops below a set temperature and switched off at a top temperature threshold. The engine intakes are heated in a similar manner, although heat transfer to the rapidly moving air entering the engine requires that the intakes are heated continuously.

The rotor blades present a greater problem. As the surface to be heated is so large, the limited power available has to be switched sequentially from one blade to another, or between diametrically opposite pairs of blades. The power applied to each blade is fed first to elements at the leading edge of the blade and then to others located progressively further across its chord. In this way ice that is melted at the leading edge cannot re-freeze as run back ice, before being thrown off by centrifugal force.

Power to the main and tail rotor blade anti-icing systems is fed to an arrangement of brushes and rotating conductors known as a slip ring assembly. The power demands for such a system are substantial as is the weight penalty of any rotor blade anti-icing system. Only where the operational task of the helicopter makes operations in icing conditions essential can the penalties of increased power generation, distribution and control be justified.

6.

The Helicopter as a Weapons Platform

The arming of helicopters dates almost from the time that helicopters first went into production. Before the end of 1944 a few German helicopters were given a 7.92-mm machine gun. The Korean War spawned some attempts to arm American helicopters but they were generally less than successful. It was hard to believe that the helicopter would ever become a weapons platform. Its instability and high vibration levels gave new meaning to the word inaccuracy and may even have given rise to the advice 'whatever you hit, call it the target'. There were only a few weapons that were even remotely suitable for installing on helicopters and these were usually heavy, bulky, inherently inaccurate, lacked range and had limited lethality; some had unacceptable recoil forces. Little thought appeared to have been given to what targets armed helicopters might usefully engage; they were seen merely as mobile sources of firepower.

The French proved in Algeria (1954–62) that helicopters armed with machine guns, free flight rockets and guided missiles could make a marked impact on a guerrilla campaign. The lessons were not lost on the Americans as they became embroiled in their war in Vietnam. At the beginning there was no alternative to attaching whatever weapons were considered appropriate to any available airframes. So was born the gunship: a utility helicopter, in this case the UH-1B, was armed with a free-flight rocket pod and a 7.62-mm machine gun on either side of the fuselage. The mounting of such weapons, however, precluded the carriage of troops or cargo, reduced manoeuvrability and so diminished maximum cruising speed that the gunships were unable to catch up with the formations they were escorting once they had left them to attack a target *en route*.

It was decided that the gunship needed a 50% excess in speed over its escorted transport helicopters. This has never been achieved for several very good reasons. Installing weapons, inevitably, has an adverse effect on a helicopter's performance and its airframe, the first of direct concern to the operator and the second to the designer.

Helicopter weapons are usually hung from below the fuselage or on outriggers or stub wings. Drag is thereby enhanced to the extent that 0.1 sq. m. of flat plate drag costs about 11 shp at 185 kph (115 mph). Eight TOW missiles, as carried on the *Lynx* for example, represent a loss of 50 shp at 185 kph. The loss increases significantly with higher speeds. The missile sight in the roof adds to the problem. The result is that speed – and the sight, missiles and outriggers reduce this in the

FIG. 6.1 The *Lynx* can carry eight TOW missiles (*Westland Helicopters*)

Lynx by about 28 kph (17 mph) – and manoeuvrability are traded for firepower.

The firing of weapons also affects the airframe. The recoil forces of guns, and blast pressure and debris at launch from rockets and missiles, must all be considered carefully by the designer. The structural stiffness of the wings and outriggers for a stable launch is a design factor; so is the ability to jettison these weapons in an emergency.

It is clear therefore that the carriage of weapons imposes certain constraints on the helicopter; on the other hand, the helicopter degrades the optimum perform-ance of its weapons.

Guns

The overriding factor when contemplating the installation of guns is the weight of the entire system. A gun system comprises the gun itself, the mounting, the fire control system, ammunition and the ammunition feed. The weight allocated to the complete system largely determines the calibre of the gun. As this increases so does the weight of all the constituent parts. Other factors to be considered include the probabilities of engagement, hit and kill (range and lethality of the weapon), the type of mounting and the type and amount of ammunition to be carried.

Guns can be fixed to the side of, or under, the fuselage to fire forwards only or in

FIG. 6.2 The *Havoc*'s 30-mm cannon fully deflected 110° to port (E. J. Everett-Heath)

gun pods on wing pylons. If mounted on the fuselage a greater number of rounds can be carried. The weapon/helicopter trade-off favours the weapon in the case of fixed forward-firing guns as the helicopter must be turned to face the target before fire can be opened; precious seconds may be lost. Furthermore, the pilot must manoeuvre the helicopter to get it into the correct pitch attitude to achieve the desired range and then he must maintain that position during the burst of fire. The pilot usually fires fixed guns (or traversable guns locked into the forward-firing mode) by means of a simple reflector sight. The recoil loads can be high enough actually to displace the helicopter in flight and so to obviate this the muzzle velocity of some guns has to be reduced; and parts of the airframe structure must be strengthened to withstand blast overpressures.

Traversable guns are mounted in the nose or below it, sometimes in a gun turret (for example, in the Soviet *Hind*) and sometimes not (the American *Apache*, for instance), or in the cabin. Sometimes known as waist or pintle-mounted guns, such latter installations are quite heavy and cumbersome, have a limited arc of fire, need a crewman to fire them, hinder troop entrance and exit and usually require the floor to be strengthened. The ammunition feed is complicated and aiming at a lateral target while in forward flight difficult. Turretted guns have a wide arc of fire, a quick reaction time and are usually linked to a fire control system through an optical or helmet-mounted sight. The fire control solution, whether computer-aided or not, must take into account such factors as the forward speed of the aircraft, its attitude, bullet drop due to gravity, range, crosswinds, airframe distortion and vibration. A high proportion of tracer rounds is essential if the helicopter has no weapons computer.

Fig. 6.3 The *Apache*'s 30-mm chain gun (*E. J. Everett-Heath*)

Guns may be single or multi-barrelled and vary in calibre from 7.62 mm to 30 mm. Whatever the calibre range is comparatively short and probably does not exceed 2,500 m for 30 mm weapons. For the attack of ground targets rates of fire of between 300 and 900 rounds a minute are quite satisfactory but against airborne, targets, e.g., helicopters, as high a rate as possible, say 4,000 rounds a minute, are required. Such a rate must be balanced against the number of rounds that can be carried and the number of engagements the helicopter may be expected to undertake without rearming. A short time of flight is also important in air-to-air combat to achieve a good probability of hit and this can be achieved by a high muzzle velocity, say about 1,000 m/s, and low projectile drag. Likely targets should be defined so that the correct type of ammunition is loaded. The *Havoc* has two ammunition boxes with separate feeds, thus allowing the gunner to select the type of ammunition he wants for a particular target.

A helicopter is less stable in the hover than in forward flight and therefore in this latter regime guns will generally be more accurate. But as they close with the target helicopters may well come into the range of their target's weapons, probably mounted on more stable platforms, or other weapons unseen in the vicinity.

Thought must be given to the location of the ammunition drums, the ammunition feed and, finally, the ejection of empty cartridge cases and clips so that they are not ingested into the engines, strike the rotor systems or foul any control linkages.

FIG. 6.4 70-mm rocket pods on a *Blackhawk* (*E. J. Everett-Heath*)

Rockets

Free flight, or unguided, rockets, like fixed guns, are fired by the pilot using his reflector sight; adjustments are necessary to cater for the ballistic trajectory. The Americans use 70-mm rockets on their *Cobra* and *Apache* while the Russians arm the *Hind* with 57-mm and 80-mm rockets. There is no reason why much larger calibre rockets, say up to 300-mm, should not be carried.

All these helicopters place the rockets in multiple-tube pods mounted under the wings, although there are other ways of installing them. Recoil is much less than that of guns and therefore the airframe suffers less.

Rockets fired in a salvo can produce a considerable weight of fire, but they are an area weapon and inherently less accurate than guns. In the past small changes in pitch attitude, either in the hover or when flying forward, resulted in large errors of range. But with new programmable electronic fuses, a laser rangefinder and wing pylons that are tilted automatically once the range has been inserted into the fire control system, accuracy has improved dramatically. The new fuses permit the so-called 'wall-in-space' technique whereby sub-munitions in a cargo warhead are ejected at a specific moment as though hitting an invisible wall; they fall nearly vertically and dispersion is reduced. Range has been increased to more than 5,000 m with new rocket motors; and new warheads to cater for different targets have raised the probability of kill given a hit.

Anti-tank Guided Missiles

As the 1960s dawned the range at which tank targets could be acquired was considerably greater than the range at which the high velocity gun of a defending

FIG. 6.5 A French Army *Gazelle* fires a HOT missile (*Euromissile*)

tank could hope to achieve a first round hit. A guided missile could not only match
the acquisition range, and thus fill the gap, but it also posed two new problems for
tank designers: tanks in future would need to have armour to protect themselves
against chemical energy weapons in addition to the traditional kinetic rounds of
tank guns. Furthermore, because helicopters could fire from different angles and
thus extend the three-dimensional arc of attack, the distribution of protective
armour would have to be rearranged.

The current second generation of missiles may be rail- or tube-launched. Tubed
missiles offer built-in storage and some protection when being handled or moved.
Some, such as TOW and HOT, developed from man-portable systems, have two
propulsion motors: a launch motor, which burns for less than a second, to get the
missile out of its tube when it then coasts until the sustainer motor cuts in. The
launch, or boost, motor must have sufficient acceleration to cope with the downwash from the main rotor. All these second generation missiles are subsonic and
usually take 17 seconds or more to reach their maximum range of between 3,500
and 4,000 m.

A missile that can be fired and then immediately forgotten is highly desirable for
obvious tactical reasons. The American *Hellfire* goes some way to meeting this
requirement and has the potential, now being developed, to meet it completely (see
p. 134). This modular missile has a laser spot-seeker in its nose and if its own
launching helicopter designates the target then the gunner must keep the laser

spot on the target until missile impact. But if a third party, either ground-based or in another helicopter, does the designating then the *Hellfire* can be fired and then ignored by the helicopter crew. Indeed, because designation is only needed during the terminal phase of the missile's flight the *Hellfire*'s seeker can lock on to its target after the missile has been launched. Lock-on after launch allows direct fire with the target beyond seeker range, or for the launching aircraft to remain behind cover with the missile following an indirect trajectory, picking up the laser spot from a ground designator or another aircraft, and then homing on to the target. The *Hellfire* system can engage multiple targets almost simultaneously. With rapid fire, using the same laser designator, a missile can be fired at the chosen target. While it is in flight a second or more missiles can be launched at the same target. As soon as the first *Hellfire* strikes the target the designator is pointed at the second target and the missile swings on to its new course to strike it. In ripple fire, two or more laser designators, using different codes preset in the missiles' seekers, allow a much faster firing rate. An obvious potential problem is matching the laser codes in the missiles to those in the remote designators.

Missiles usually suffer from having a tell-tale smoke signature on launch which may give away the position of the launching helicopter.

Armour protection is continually being improved by various means and to match these improvements missile designers have to enhance the penetration and killing power of their warheads or try to attack the target where it is less well protected, or preferably both. In the direct fire lock-on before launch mode the *Hellfire* automatically climbs so that it can dive onto its target. When locking-on after launch, the co-pilot/gunner has a choice of trajectory, both entailing a terminal dive: low, to

FIG. 6.6 A *Havoc* with eight *spiral* anti-tank missile tubes and a pod for 20 × 80-mm rockets (*E. J. Everett-Heath*)

FIG. 6.7 An *Apache* with eight *Hellfire* missiles and 38 × 70-mm rockets
(*McDonnell Douglas*)

prevent losing lock-on if the missile were to enter cloud, or high, to clear terrain
obstacles. The well-tried TOW is now being developed further to give it the ability
to attack its target from overhead – top attack. The American version is known as
TOW 2B and the British FITOW (Further Improvements to TOW). The TOW 2B

will have a dual mode sensor and two warheads. The missile will fly over the target and the sensor will activate the two warheads at precisely the correct moments, the first to trigger the explosive reactive armour now found on modern Soviet tanks and the second to penetrate the main armour. Missile launchers will have to be modified for the TOW 2B and it is possible that this will not be considered cost-effective for the *Cobra* but only for ground-based launchers. FITOW employs a downward-looking active laser proximity fuse to initiate two shaped charge warheads which will penetrate their target's upper surface. The vertical impact will permit the attack of tanks even when they are hull-down. The Euromissile HOT 2T is also being developed to defeat explosive reactive armour by means of a tandem warhead and proximity fuse.

A third generation, anti-tank missile is the Euromissile Dynamics Group's TRIGAT, also known as PARS-3 in West Germany and AC3G in France. The three countries are collaborating on medium-range and long-range versions of this missile. The long-range, helicopter-borne variant will replace TOW, HOT and *Swingfire* and is expected to enter service in 1998. It will be truly fire-and-forget with a nose-mounted passive homing imaging infra-red seeker, which will lock-on before launch, and a tandem charge warhead. The gunner's missile sight, possibly mast-mounted, will be able to track four targets simultaneously. With a range of 4,500 m, which it will reach in about seventeeeen seconds, the missile will dive at an

FIG. 6.8 A *Hind* E with, from left to right, an empty pylon, an 80-mm rocket pod,
a 57-mm rocket pod and a bomb

approximate angle of 30 degrees onto its target, although, if engaging other helicopters, it can be fired along a direct flight path.

Air-to-Air Missiles

The installation of air-to-air missiles on helicopters has been under study and trial for at least 15 years. No such missile specifically designed for helicopters has yet appeared, the favoured route to this capability being the adaptation of shoulder-launched surface-to-air missiles (SAM), such as *Stinger*, or less common,

FIG. 6.9 The Italian A.129 *Mangusta* (*Agusta*)

air-to-air missiles (AAM) such as *Sidewinder*. The Yugoslav Air Force has equipped some of its Gazelles and the Polish Air Force some of its Mi-2 Hoplites with the Soviet SA-7 shoulder-launched missile.

The adaptation of ground-launched missiles is no simple matter. Even if hovering, the helicopter is not stationary; missile launch must cope with the problems of vibration, rotor downwash, possibly crosswinds and electromagnetic compatibility. Additionally, it must be possible to launch the missile with the helicopter on the ground, in the hover or up to its maximum speed in forward or sideways flight, and when rolling, pitching and yawing. The designer must resolve these problems while minimising the inevitable limitations on the helicopter and the missile.

Other Weapons

Only the Soviet Union and a few client states use helicopters to drop bombs up to 500 kg (1100 lb). The carriage, launch and sighting requirements are comparatively simple. The bombs fall under gravity or are retarded by means of a parachute.

The Americans used 40 mm grenade launchers, firing at a rate of 400 a minute, during the Vietnam War. They do not do so now. The Russians, however, have been reported as using smaller calibre grenade launchers from their helicopters. The Russians also carry anti-personnel mine dispensers on the weapons pylons of the *Hind* and *Hip*. The *Hip* also lays anti-tank mines by means of a chute protruding from the rear of the cargo hold.

Although no helicopters are currently equipped with hypervelocity missiles it is quite possible that some will be within the foreseeable future. They could be used against both tanks and helicopters. A speed of about 2,000 m/s is attainable. Guidance could be laser beam-riding.

Other Factors

It will be already obvious that to integrate weapon systems with helicopters is a complicated business. To the factors already mentioned it is necessary to add the demands of safety and airworthiness; the degree of self-test before take-off; and the design of the weapon launcher to permit reliable and safe launch under all conditions, to minimise drag and to facilitate rapid reload, preferably without any additional equipment.

Armed or Attack Helicopters?

There are not many different types of genuine attack helicopter in service worldwide. While there is a considerable number of armed helicopters only the Mi-24 *Hind* E and F, the Italian A.129 *Mangusta*, the American AH-1 *Cobra* and AH-64 *Apache* can claim to be attack helicopters. These are examined in some detail in Chapter 9. Under study or active research and development, however, are five more: the Soviet Mi-28 *Havoc* and the Kamov *Hokum* (both in the flight test stage),

FIG. 6.10 A West German Army *Bo-105* with six HOT missiles (*MBB*)

the American LHX, the Anglo-Italian *Tonal* and the Franco-German PAH-2/ HAC/HAP, now known as the *Tiger*.

Attack helicopters are limited in the roles that they can undertake, since they are usually two-seaters and have no cabin; the *Hind* however, is an exception with a cabin for eight troops and the Havoc has a small bay at the forward end of the tailboom in which up to three people, from a downed aircraft perhaps, can be flown to safety. Attack helicopters are designed to survive in a hostile environment and to attack a variety of targets. They are inevitably expensive therefore, and those countries which cannot afford them take the alternative course of arming utility or reconnaissance helicopters, such as the *Lynx*, the French *Gazelle* and the German Bo-105. In any armoured warfare these helicopters are normally employed in counter-penetration tasks. Such utility helicopters, when unarmed, offer advantages that attack helicopters cannot match: they can evacuate casualties, lift troops and supplies and act as airborne command posts, all useful attributes in such places as Northern Ireland and Hong Kong.

Despite the role flexibility of armed helicopters, the need for attack helicopters is widely recognised and more and more countries are now in the process of procuring them.

Missile Sights and Guidance

It could be argued that a weapon is only as good as its associated sight and method of guidance. Certainly they are a vital part of any weapon system. The most common form of missile guidance is known as semi-automatic command to line-of-sight (SACLOS). To hit the target all that is required of the gunner is to keep the sight's cross hairs on the target until missile impact. An infra-red beacon in the aft end of the missile is tracked by a device on the helicopter and any deviations from the line-of-sight to the target are passed to the helicopter's command electronics pack which calculates the necessary course corrections. These are sent automatically, either by means of a wire link or by radio, to the missile's control system which responds to bring the missile back onto the gunner's line-of-sight. Radio command can of course be jammed but this form of guidance allows shorter times of flight because no wires, which restrict speed to about 250–280 m/s, have to be paid out behind the missile.

Before a missile can be fired it must be roughly aligned with the target and the helicopter must be in a more or less stable attitude, thus limiting its freedom to manoeuvre. Post-launch constraints are less demanding but any substantial manoeuvring will make it difficult, if not impossible, for the gunner to keep the cross hairs of the sight, although stabilised, on the target during the flight of the missile. During this time the launching helicopter is susceptible to detection and engagement by the target or other weapon systems within range.

Currently, most missile sights are in or under the nose or in the roof of the cockpit. Despite the disadvantages, however, we may see in the future more sights mounted above the mast. The first operational helicopter to have such a sight is the

FIG. 6.11 The mast-mounted sight of the *OH-58D* (*E. J. Everett-Heath*)

American OH-58D. Its sight includes a day TV camera, a thermal imager, a laser rangefinder and a designator for its own and the Apache's *Hellfires*. Its sight line is about 80 cm (32 in) above the plane of the rotor and some 1.8 m (6 ft) above the observer's eye line. The tactical advantages are clear. The sensor package above the mast weighs 64 kg (141 lb) but it has not made a major difference to the flying qualities of the helicopter although it has added to the drag. Being located above the mast there are no direct view optics, the observer having a CRT in front of him on which to view the scene. By day target acquisition is by means of the TV with a 2° × 8° wide field of view; at night or in obscured conditions by means of the thermal imager in a 3° × 10° field of view.

To allow the *Apache* to fly and fight at night and in reduced visibility it has a unique Pilot Night Vision Sensor (PNVS) and a Target Acquisition and Designation Sight (TADS). They are mounted in the nose, the PNVS being the smaller system above the TADS. They are described in Chapter 9.

The laser-seeking *Hellfire* fired by means of the TADS is not 'fire and forget'. When fitted with a radio frequency seeker and allied to a millimetre wave fire control radar, however, it becomes so. Furthermore, a millimetre wave radar has the ability to penetrate heavy rain, smoke and fog which optical seekers find difficult. Operating on a frequency of either 35 GHz or 94 GHz, millimetre wave offers very good resolution though it is limited in range. The *Apache's* use of the Airborne Adverse Weather Weapon System using a millimetre wave fire control radar is also described in Chapter 9.

Summary

Over the years the helicopter has evolved from an *ad hoc* weapons platform to a fully integrated weapon system capable of operating by day and night in all but the worst weather. Its ability to deploy faster than any other battlefield system to combat unexpected incursions by armour or attack helicopters is a characteristic

TABLE 6.1
Missile Characteristics

	ITOW	HOT	HELLFIRE	SPIRAL	LR TRIGAT
Country	USA	FRANCE	USA	USSR	FR/GE/UK
Max. range (m) (direct fire)	3750	4000	5000	5000	4500
Time of flight (s)	21	17	?	11	17
Weight (kg)	18	23.5	43	31	40
Guidance	Wire	Wire	Laser	Radio	IR Homing
Platform	Lynx	Gazelle/Bo-105	Apache	Hind	Tonal/Tiger

	Stinger	SA-7
Country	USA	USSR
Max. height (m)	4800	4830
Speed (m/s)	575	580
Weight (kg)	15.8	9.2
Guidance	IR	IR
Platform	OH-58D/Apache	Mi-2 Hoplite/Yugoslav Gazelle

which, in conjunction with its increasingly effective weapons, can make a substantial contribution to the land battle. Second generation attack helicopters, with their more potent weapons, advanced sensors and enhanced survivability, pose an ever greater threat to armoured formations and to the enemy's rear areas. Imaginative use of this still comparatively new weapon system could well give commanders the advantages provided first by the cavalry, then by tanks: the ability to achieve surprise and a shock effect.

7.

Survivability

The Problem

The equipment designers of today face the same problems of balancing the triangle of armaments, mobility and protection that mediaeval knights once faced. With only shield, mail tunic and helmet they were vulnerable to the lance, doubled-edged sword and mace, but being light and agile they stood a fair chance of avoiding the blows. Armour was later seen as a good way of reducing that vulnerability, but hand-in-hand with that protection came a loss of manoeuvrability and a greater likelihood of being hit. This is a similar problem to that met in the design of armoured vehicles and dealt with in some detail in Volume 7 of this series.

Until recently, power and other limitations in light battlefield helicopters dictated that the available payload should be used for fuel and role equipment, thus allowing only the minimum of armour protection. The helicopter was a 'soft-skinned' vehicle, but some reduction in vulnerability could be achieved by capitalising on its speed and agility, backed up by the use of good tactics and fieldcraft: in the helicopter this means making the most of terrain screening in very low level flight. But as combat helicopters became more effective, so countermeasures against them grew in scope, quality and quantity. Helicopters were prey to enemy armed helicopters, air-defence guns and missiles, vehicle-mounted weapons, small arms, massed artillery and multiple rocket fire. Fixed-wing aircraft, particularly slow-flying, also posed a threat.

Clearly something had to be done to redress the balance, to allow the helicopter to continue fighting or, if this were not possible, to permit its return to base for repairs. Put another way, the helicopter designer was given the tasks, in order of priority, of saving the man, the machine and the mission.

It is not difficult to appreciate then that survivability depends on the product of a number of probabilities. In simple terms, what is required is a combat helicopter that is difficult to detect, difficult to hit when it has been detected, capable of continuing the mission even when it has been hit, and crashworthy if it is shot down. To achieve all these objectives would be expensive and add weight which would conflict with flight performance; some compromises have to be made as regards helicopter design and the survivability equipment installed.

With a full suite of warning devices, countermeasures (including weapons), and protective measures (including armour plating), the helicopter would inevitably be large and heavy; it would therefore need powerful engines and an associated transmission system. It follows that the overall cost of the helicopter would be high and one element of the eternal triangle, mobility/manoeuvrability, would probably suffer.

Detection

Tactical Measures

Leaving aside the problems of indirect enemy fire where a helicopter can be hit unseen by the weapon crew (a matter about which the crew can do little apart from anticipate where such fire might fall), a helicopter has to be seen to be hit. This involves a direct line of sight between the observer or sensor and the target. Minimising exposure to the enemy is, therefore, a fundamental measure in improving the chances of survival. Cover from enemy observation may be achieved by flying very low, below the enemy's horizon, and by making maximum use of the terrain. This is standard NATO practice; the Russians, however, for historical, topographical and strategic reasons do not try to avoid detection but use other methods to ensure the completion of the mission.

Positioning of Sights

The importance of sights was mentioned in the last chapter. Besides their primary function they also contribute to survivability because they allow the helicopter to stand back from the enemy. Survivability is a factor when considering where sights should be positioned on the airframe. Obviously, if located under the nose (Mi-24 *Hind* and Mi-28 *Havoc*) or in it (AH-1F *Cobra*, AH-64 *Apache* and A-129 *Mangusta*) practically the entire helicopter must expose itself to observe or fire. If the sight is in the cockpit roof (Bo-105, *Gazelle*, *Lynx*) exposure is reduced, but best of all is the sight mounted above the rotor mast (OH-58D).

FIG. 7.1 The *Hind*'s sight is the larger assembly under the forward cockpit on the starboard side

Fig. 7.2 A mast-mounted sight reduces exposure (*McDonnell Douglas*)

Missiles

The vulnerability of the helicopter also depends to a certain degree on the type of anti-armour missile carried. Helicopters with true fire-and-forget missiles will not have to unmask for long to aim and fire, unlike those with missiles which have to be guided on to the target and which are therefore at risk throughout the flight of the missile. In this instance, of course, the speed of the missile and therefore the time of flight is important.

Signatures

A helicopter has five distinctive signatures by which its presence may be detected: visual, acoustic, radar, infra-red and electronic. A degree of passive defence can be achieved by suppressing these signatures with the aim of making the helicopter all but undetectable at the maximum range of its weapons; by controlling them the effectiveness of active countermeasures is enhanced.

VISUAL SIGNATURE

Visual detection is achieved by the unaided eye, optical instruments, such as binoculars and image intensifiers, or television. How successful these are depends on the size and shape of the helicopter, its contrast with the background and movement. Obviously the smaller the machine the harder it is to see. Paint schemes can reduce the contrast with the background and help to produce an illusory shape. Matt paint, where it can be used, eliminates shine. Movement tends to attract attention and, even when in the hover, the sun glinting on the canopy or

FIG. 7.3 The latest versions of the *Cobra* have a flat plate canopy
(*E. J. Everett-Heath*)

FIG. 7.4 Rotor downwash (*Rolls-Royce*)

the rotor may give the helicopter's position away. Some helicopters such as the *Cobra*, the *Apache*, the Italian *Mangusta* and the *Havoc* have flat plate canopies to reduce sustained glint to momentary flashes; the appropriate paint can minimise rotor flicker. The condition of the ground's surface is an important factor when in the hover because sand, dust, snow or leaves, recirculated through the main rotor, can betray the presence of a helicopter. The strength of the rotor downwash is germane to this problem and is certainly a factor in the design of a combat helicopter. An experienced observer can deduce the presence of a helicopter, even if he cannot see or hear it, purely from branches moving when there is little or no wind.

ACOUSTIC SIGNATURE

It is often claimed that the acoustic signature of a combat helicopter is relatively unimportant since the battlefield is not known for its solitude. Nevertheless, there are occasions, such as during the covert infiltration or recovery of patrols and in certain counter-insurgency operations, when stealth is essential. Because a specific type of helicopter can be identified by its acoustic signature it is possible that in the future its sound may be used to trigger mines designed to destroy it. Some of the noise may be attenuated by terrain features, but the presence of a helicopter will be obvious and a trained observer may have time to ready his weapon and assess the probable flight path before the helicopter becomes visible. The biggest contributors to noise are the main and the tail rotor and engines. Many Soviet helicopters have rotors which turn at slow speed and therefore with the consequently low tip speed

FIG. 7.5 The swept rotor blade tip and canted tail rotor of the *Black Hawk*
(*E. J. Everett-Heath*)

have relatively low noise signatures. Blade tip shapes also help in this respect: both the *Apache* and the UH-60 *Black Hawk* have aft swept tips. So does the British ASP blade, described in Chapter 8. Helicopters which do not have tail rotors, such as those from the Soviet Kamov bureau and the McDonnell Douglas NOTAR (No Tail Rotor) helicopter, are inherently quieter than conventional machines. The *Apache* and the *Havoc* have offset tail rotor blades which, besides being more efficient, are also less noisy.

RADAR SIGNATURE

A target illuminated by radar produces a signature known as radar reflectivity or radar cross-section. The amount of energy reflected is a function of target size, shape, angle relative to the beam, material electrical properties and the characteristics of the radar itself.

Detection thus depends upon the radar and its processing of information, the target's signature and the skill of the operator in interpreting what he can see on his screen. A radar's detection range and its ability to find helicopters in ground clutter can be degraded by reductions in the helicopter's radar cross-section. Control of the shape of the helicopter and use of the appropriate radar-absorbent materials in its structure are two basic methods of achieving this. Radar-transparent materials in the aircraft's skin and rotor blades, however, need to be 'metallised' to eliminate radar reflections from internal components. Taking into account where possible the most probable angles from which the helicopter will be seen on radar, shapes can be chosen, subject to other design constraints, which can reflect the energy anywhere but back to the radar.

Doppler radars detect motion. But even in the hover the helicopter has many moving parts, such as rotors and hubs, and these can be picked up by such a radar even though the helicopter is hiding behind trees. The use of certain coatings and broadband radar-absorbing material can lower the risk.

INFRA-RED SIGNATURE

Any object with a temperature above absolute zero radiates infra-red (IR) energy. Because of atmospheric absorption this energy appears in the 1–3, 3–5 and 8–13 micron wavelengths. The hot metal in a helicopter engine emits in the lowest band while the engine exhaust gases are in the middle band. The first generation of engine exhaust suppressors consisted merely of scoops to deflect the exhaust upwards into the rotor downwash and to shield the hot metal from the direct view of an IR-seeking missile. More modern suppressors use large quantities of ambient air to cool the hot metal and to dilute the exhaust gas to lower its temperature. Hot parts of the engine, such as the turbine discs, are obscured from view by good exhaust duct design. All these measures are known together as the 'black hole' system and it is needed to cater for the more modern and sophisticated missiles such as *Stinger*.

IR low-reflective paint can also be used to reduce the likelihood of detection and to decrease the effective range of heat-seeking missiles; it also helps to increase the effectiveness of IR jammers and decoy flares.

Fig. 7.6 Exhaust gas suppressors on a *Lynx* (*E. J. Everett-Heath*)

Miscellaneous Electromagnetic Emitters

There are many items of equipment on board a helicopter which by their use will give its position away. Direction finders can pinpoint radio emissions; target acquisition and ranging radars, Doppler navigators, radar altimeters, laser range-finders/designators and, indeed, any other active systems are all liable to detection. They must therefore be used as infrequently as possible, voice communications kept to the minimum and the helicopter kept on the move as far as possible in dead ground.

Detection on the Ground

Before we leave the matter of detection it is as well to remember that combat helicopters spend more time on the ground than they do in the air. Concealment and camouflage are therefore essential and not only from ground observation but also from the view of an enemy reconnaissance pilot, the sensors on-board his aircraft and all other target acquisition devices, such as remotely-piloted vehicles and drones. Concealment from thermal imagers probably poses the greatest difficulties. Skid-equipped helicopters are difficult to move, those with wheels a little less so, and all types are cumbersome to camouflage, principally because of the rotor systems. Because it was designed as a ship-based ASW helicopter, the EH-101 in its utility version will also have folding main rotor blades which will facilitate concealment in the field. Apart from this, no satisfactory solutions have been found to overcome these problems, despite combat helicopters having been in service for many years.

Engagement

Tactics

Although a helicopter may be detected, the crew can use certain techniques and procedures to minimise the chances of their being hit. The most obvious way is to get out of sight of the enemy as quickly as possible, thus providing insufficient time for them to aim their weapons. This can be done by using dead ground or any available cover. When exposure is inevitable, either to observe or to fire, then this should be carried out from a concealed ambush position and followed by an immediate move to another location. By opening fire at maximum effective range further problems will be created for the enemy, although it should be remembered that staying out of range of the target may bring the helicopter within range of other enemy weapon systems. The big problem for the helicopter crew is knowing when they have been detected. Like infantry or armour, combat helicopters should use fire and movement and operate in close co-ordination with the ground forces, fixed-wing aircraft and other helicopters.

Manoeuvrability

While speed is important in certain circumstances, and is favoured by the Warsaw Pact, manoeuvrability, or the ability to change the velocity vector, and agility, or the time required to do this, are more highly prized by NATO. This simply means acceleration and deceleration in all dimensions, very often from the hover. A power margin that permits a rapid rate of climb when above cover and an ability to descend and establish a new hover quickly without striking the ground is required, even when the helicopter is at maximum weight. In addition, a helicopter must be able to accelerate sideways to avoid bursts of fire and even to fly backwards safely. When considering air-to-air combat two of the most important flight performance characteristics are the rate of roll at high and low speeds and positive yaw control. High rates of roll, including the reversal of the turn from one direction to another, allow the pilot to get on to the tail of his target or to avoid his pursuer. A very crisp response to inputs to the flight controls is therefore essential. Combat helicopters should be able to sustain turns at 3 G and also accept up to -1 G for five seconds or so.

Warning Sensors

To see without being seen is the ideal; the reverse may lead to disaster. Warning the crew of the presence of enemy weapon systems, therefore, plays a large part in the avoidance of being hit. A radar warning receiver, which can provide an immediate indication of a radar associated with a weapon system that threatens the helicopter, will alert the crew to the danger. A receiver that can detect surveillance, missile guidance and tracking radars and display which associated weapon systems pose the greatest threats in order of priority is necessary. It must have 360° coverage and give a visual and aural warning.

Interpretation of the display was a problem with the early receivers, there being no doubt that the crew must be able to form an accurate mental picture of the

FIG. 7.7 The forward radar warning antennae on a Royal Navy *Lynx*
(*E. J. Everett-Heath*)

situation from a single glance; range cannot be measured, but, in any case, it is less important than the direction of the radar. Modern receivers are programmable before take-off to cater for only the anticipated threat radars.

The advent of directed-energy weapons is not far off. Laser dazzle from laser sensor damage weapons, which should be relatively cheap and light, have no 'ammunition' limit and with a virtually instantaneous time of flight, will pose a serious threat to crews' eyes and degrade electro-optical sensors; laser damage weapons will yellow and craze canopies. Thus a laser warning receiver will soon be necessary to detect and identify all types of threatening laser. One of the major problems is that laser beams can be very narrow and therefore the choice of the receiver antenna position will require careful thought. Another problem may be identification of the laser or, in other words, what its purpose is: rangefinder, designator, laser beam along which a missile may ride, sensor damage weapon or damage weapon? The crew's eyes may be protected by using a special anti-laser visor on the helmet but this inevitably reduces light levels to the eye. Counter-measures to lasers include the inserting of filters into the sights and the use of new materials resistant to laser energy in the construction of windshields and canopies.

If decoy flares or chaff are to be used only when there is a missile to be decoyed and not just fired off at regular intervals when a threat might exist, then some sort of warning device is required. Obviously its reaction time between detecting the missile and automatically dispensing the flares or chaff must be shorter than the time required by the missile to reach the target. Thus the detection of the launch of a missile is to be preferred to the information that it is already on its way. Current missile approach warners use an active Doppler radar.

What are more difficult to warn against are those threat systems which are not radiating: any concealed operator who is merely using his eyes, binoculars or other optical aids has a distinct advantage and every helicopter crew must guard against blundering into areas where visually sited weapons may be brought to bear. Work is proceeding on the development of optical warning devices but progress is slow. Warning of small arms and machine gun fire can be achieved by acoustic means but so far no system has been considered reliable enough or sufficiently cost-effective, and there may be good psychological reasons for not proceeding with further development of such systems.

Wires can bring down a helicopter in war or peace. Thorough flight planning and careful and continuous lookout are essential. Electronic means of detecting wires have been under study for a number of years and millimetric wave radars and lasers have been the most promising. Stabilisation in relation to the helicopter's constantly changing attitude in flight and psychological factors, however, pose problems. Simple wire cutters, such as those on the OH-58, and deflectors may be the solution. Cutters should be capable of slicing through steel-stranded wires up to at least 1 cm in diameter.

FIG. 7.8 Wire cutters above and below the cockpit of a Swedish Army OH-58
(*E. J. Everett-Heath*)

Countermeasures

Receiving timely warning of a threat is one thing, but the consequent reaction is what is important. Descending or turning away could be all that is needed, but active countermeasures may be more effective. The most positive is to open fire on the offending system, if appropriate; if not, radar or IR jamming or the dispensing of chaff or decoy flares could cause sufficient degradation to prevent the helicopter from being hit.

Chaff consists of a mass of very small dipole reflectors, cut to some frequency equal to or lower than the radar frequency, which are dispensed in sufficient quantity to saturate the radar receiver. To match the very high frequencies of modern radars the dipoles are very small and so one chaff cartridge can contain several thousand. However, enough cartridges must be fired to ensure that the chaff cloud produces a larger return than the helicopter. Launched as soon as a tracking radar locks on to the helicopter, the chaff has the effect of breaking the lock and forcing the radar operator to return to the search mode to re-establish lock-on. This takes time during which the crew can take evasive action or open fire. Ideally combined with a radar warning receiver, chaff can be dispensed automatically and in the correct direction. A cockpit control unit allows crew selection of the dispensing mode, the number of units to be fired, the interval between units and groups of units, and group intervals. A typical dispenser can contain 60 chaff cartridges.

IR decoy flares are perhaps in more common use. Pictures of Israeli aircraft over Lebanon and Soviet aircraft, including helicopters, over Afghanistan showed them regularly dispensing flares to decoy any heat-seeking missiles that might be fired against them. Soviet-built *Hinds* and *Hips*, operating in many trouble spots around the world, initially had flare dispensers strapped to the bottom of the aft end of the tailboom. In some cases these have been superseded by a dispenser on either side of the forward end of the tailboom, angled to fire forwards and slightly upwards. Simply producing a hotter signature than the target helicopter is no longer enough; a flare that matches the helicopter's IR signature and generates greater heat, together with an effective launching system and simultaneous evasive manoeuvres are needed. Furthermore, the decoy must remain active throughout the time that the missile is a threat.

To be cost-effective in a helicopter, jammers must be small, light, affordable, powerful enough to jam the target system and able to cope with the vibration inherent in a helicopter. Nevertheless, more and more helicopters are now being fitted with an IR jammer. Electrically operated and omnidirectional, it may consist of a cylindrical source which emits modulated IR energy several times greater than that of the helicopter itself to confuse the missile's IR seeker. Jammers should be able to cope with two missiles operating in different wavebands simultaneously and be programmable to cater for future threats.

Radar jammers have been in use since the Second World War but until recently have been too large, heavy and complex for employment in helicopters. They should be able to jam two radars simultaneously and remain passive until illuminated by an enemy radar which has locked on to its target. They then automatically analyse the incoming signals and determine from their character-

FIG. 7.9 Most helicopter IR jammers are located above the forward end of the
tailboom

istics whether they emanate from an enemy radar. If so, electronic countermeasures are applied to defeat the range and angle measurement circuits in the
radar.

A variety of smokes might be able to provide some sort of self-defence. A green or
brown smoke to blend in with the background could provide simple screening from
enemy view, while other types may degrade laser beams and IR seekers. These,
however, need comparatively large particles to negate the IR radiation and, as a
result, they generally do not remain suspended in the air for long enough.

Tolerance to Fire

When designing a helicopter which is to tolerate fire it is vital to be clear about
the type against which protection is required and its purpose. If the helicopter is
close to a nuclear burst there is probably little that can be done, depending on the
distance from it, besides providing an arbitrary level of protection against blast,
heat and flying debris. If a missile strikes then luck will generally dictate whether
the crew can do anything to save the helicopter or themselves. Measures should
however be taken to ensure that the helicopter keeps flying if the missile detonates
outside the lethal blast area. Protection against 7.62-mm, 12.7-mm, 14.5-mm and
even isolated 23-mm API and HEI rounds is possible although neither simple nor
cheap in the case of multiple hits from a burst of even 12.7-mm machine gun fire.
Designers are usually informed of the degree of protection required against
various calibres at chosen ranges, i.e., 7.62-mm at 100 metres or 12.7-mm at 800
metres, in the form of a percentage probability of being able to continue flight for a
specific period, say 20 minutes, after having been hit.

In decreasing order of effectiveness an enemy desires to: destroy the helicopter and kill the crew, or force it to land immediately, or prevent it from continuing with its mission.

The user, and therefore the helicopter designer, is keen to deny any degree of satisfaction to the enemy. But the first priority is to save the crew; to save the mission the appropriate role equipment must remain operational. Inevitably trade-offs will arise in the degree of protection against cost, complexity, space and weight. Designers endeavour to keep the most vulnerable areas as compact as possible and to spread out duplicated and triplicated components and systems to minimise the chances of total failure. But this redundancy could mean a larger helicopter and thereby increase the risk of detection.

Tolerance to fire is best considered at the design stage when ballistic tolerance, redundancy and separation, armour plating and fire suppression can be assessed. Immunity to the smaller calibres can now be achieved for many parts of a helicopter. Composite materials offer advantages in this respect. A Kevlar fibreglass shield with high blast and 23-mm fragment resistance separates the pilot from the copilot/gunner in the *Apache* to minimise the chances of both crew members being incapacitated by the same burst of fire from the front. Both cockpits in the *Apache* and the *Hind*, for example, have spall-resistant windshields. The Russians claim that the entire canopy for both crew members in the *Havoc* is similarly resistant.

Another form of tolerance is to build transmission systems which can continue to operate for at least 30 minutes after lubricating oil has been lost.

Redundancy is attractive for reasons of safety in peacetime, apart from the benefits in war. Duplicated, or even triplicated systems which are separated confer

FIG. 7.10 The *Apache* has well separated engines (*McDonnell Douglas*)

a large measure of survivability. Engines, electrical, hydraulic and fuel systems and flight controls can all be, at the least, duplicated.

Fly-by-wire systems, which use electrical impulses through a wire from the pilot's controls to operate control jacks, are taking over from mechanical controls. They are much lighter, allowing duplication for a minimal increase in weight; being much smaller they can be widely separated, thus adding to the helicopter's survivability.

If protection is taken to the ultimate then the helicopter will survive – but it will not be able to do anything else. If armour plating is to be used then it must be used sparingly and incorporated at the design/development stage if the helicopter's weight is not to rise steeply and the centre of gravity altered. Collocated engines usually have an armoured separation plate and crews may have armoured floors, seats and body armour which must not be too bulky. The problem is to find a type of armour that is sufficiently effective at the same time as being light, easy to shape and affordable. Ceramic armour together with a glass-reinforced plastic (GRP) backing material is usually favoured. The ceramic, being very hard, causes the projectile to shatter on impact although itself disintegrating; the GRP backing absorbs the shock by delamination and picks up any small splinters that may have penetrated the ceramic. A problem yet to be solved is how to protect the crew's heads.

Fuel fires or explosions are likely to be catastrophic. Every effort then must be made to prevent their occurring or, failing this, suppressing them as quickly as

FIG. 7.11 Extra armour plate has been added to protect the cockpit sides of this
Hind F (*E. J. Everett-Heath*)

possible. Fuel tanks and lines can incorporate a material which automatically seals holes to prevent leakage, and they can be surrounded by void-filling foam or fibre material which reduces the onset of conditions which could trigger an explosion. A high speed fire-suppression system which reacts to the strike of a projectile, rather than to an excessive temperature, reduces the chances of a fire taking hold or of an explosion.

Crashworthiness

A great deal of effort in recent years has been devoted to the problems of saving the crew and limiting the damage to the aircraft to the extent that it can be repaired in the event of a crash. Crashworthy design criteria have been formulated and British military helicopters must be designed to ensure that the crew can survive a 95th percentile crash; that is 95% of all body weights surviving 95% of all crashes. In general terms, a designer has five crash-survivability objectives. They are, firstly, to maintain a protective shell around the crew and passengers; second, to make the interior of this shell injury-free; third, to limit the G load on the occupants; fourth, to prevent a post-crash fire; and finally to allow immediate escape.

To maintain a protective shell, mass items, such as engines, must withstand certain impact velocities at peak and average levels of deceleration longitudinally, laterally and vertically. MIL-STD-1290 requires a forward velocity of 15 m/s (49 ft/s), a lateral velocity of 9 m/s (30 ft/s) and a vertical impact of 12.8 m/s (42 ft/s) to be tolerated. The airframe structure should provide roll-over protection and the landing gear should be sufficiently energy-absorbing to help in the deceleration process; wheels are better than skids in this respect. The ability of main rotor blades to slice through trees of up to about 10 cm (4 in) in diameter also contributes to survival and aircraft repair. All interior equipment must be restrained to high G loads. Occupants must be positioned so that they will be free from head strikes and from being trapped or cut on sharp edges.

Limiting the load on the occupants is achieved by crash-attenuating seats which may have a movement of about 0.3 m (12 in). Five-belt safety harnesses stop the risk of slipping free.

The only practical way to prevent a post-crash fire is to contain the fuel. This can be achieved by having sufficiently strong tanks that are positioned well away from ignition sources and anything that might penetrate them in a crash. Fuel and vent lines must be crash-resistant with self-sealing break-away valves. Fuel spillage can be minimised by installing suction fuel pumps.

Safety harnesses with a single-point buckle allow rapid release and emergency escape through jettisonable doors or windows. Ejection seats are feasible, but the problems associated with jettisoning the main rotor first or ejecting sideways have so far proved to be impracticable. Warsaw Pact helicopter crews carry parachutes which they use if they have sufficient height and believe that the aircraft is doomed. Whirling rotors, projections on the airframe and its probably unstable attitude make this a hazardous pastime. In NATO, on the other hand, the thrust of survival technology has been directed towards surviving a crash.

FIG. 7.12 The crashworthy troop seats in a *Black Hawk* (*E. J. Everett-Heath*)

Battle Damage Repair

If it is possible to recover the crashed helicopter it may be possible to repair and return it to flying status. In war speed of repair is vital and therefore a degraded performance may well have to be accepted. Having the right materials and tools and a high level of training in unconventional methods of repair will be essential.

Summary

Survivability in a combat helicopter is a function of many interrelated factors, which include the threat, tactics, training, aircraft performance, target acquisition and engagement, command and control, and survivability equipment. Survivability for its own sake is valueless: the helicopter and its crew must survive in order to carry out their battlefield tasks so that they can contribute to the all-arms battle.

Survivability for attack helicopters can be measured by such exchange ratios as the number of targets destroyed per helicopter loss, and, for reconnaissance helicopters, by the length of time on task per helicopter loss.

Inevitably survivability equipment adds to the weight and cost of a helicopter, consumes space and electrical power and affects the centre of gravity and performance. These penalties must be assessed against the degree of protection provided to reach an optimum package, and this package must then be balanced against any deleterious effects that it may have on aircraft performance and the weapons and fuel load. There could come a point when the helicopter is so well protected that it loses effectiveness in its primary roles.

It is then for the military and financial staffs to decide whether it is better to go to war with a comparatively cheap and cheerful helicopter, relying largely on stealth and agility to survive, or a heavy, well-protected and expensive machine that can trade blow for blow with the enemy. National resources will dictate the answer and, for all but the Superpowers, this probably lies somewhere between the two extremes.

8.

Advanced Features and Future Trends

The State of Technology

Since the end of the Second World War, the military helicopter has benefited from the quickening technological revolution. The results have been a vastly enhanced flight performance, formidable firepower, reduced vulnerability to enemy fire, significant advances in avionics and a reduction in maintenance requirements; most important, the ever-upward spiral of production and operating costs has been slowed. The introduction of the gas turbine produced an important advance in terms of power-to-weight ratio and reliability compared with its piston predecessors. Transmissions and drive trains have progressed in their power handling capacity from 180 hp to 13,000 hp. In the 1940s rotor blades were composed of laminated wood and fabric, in the 1960s of steel and aluminium, and in the 1980s of titanium and composite materials.

In terms of sophistication, the helicopter is almost in a position to challenge the fixed-wing aircraft, and this state of affairs has been achieved in just 45 years, compared with the 85 years since the Wright brothers first flew. The helicopter now stands on the threshold of another period of dynamic technical and tactical growth. The widespread use of composite materials, fuel-efficient engines, advanced systems to reduce pilot workload and to allow operations at night and in adverse weather conditions, and novel configurations could produce a revolution in helicopter utilisation. It is probably true to say that there is no part of a helicopter that is not the subject of research or development work somewhere. In this chapter some examples of advanced features that may be retrofitted into existing helicopters or designed into the next generation of military rotorcraft are discussed.

Engine and Airframe Developments

In general terms, the total weight of a helicopter is made up of three roughly equal parts. These are: the weight of the structure and role equipment, the weight of the engine and fuel, and, making up the total all-up-weight, the payload. As with other aerial vehicles, the total all-up-weight must not exceed a certain maximum value. Within this value, however, there is some flexibility. For example, if long range is required, some of the payload can be replaced by fuel; or, if a large payload needs to be carried for a short distance, fuel can be removed and the weight saved used to carry more payload. The sum of fuel and payload is therefore known as disposable load, the individual components being varied from mission to mission.

Aerodynamic improvements, some of which will be described in more detail later, can offer increases in rotor lift and also in aircraft manoeuvrability. It should be noted that an increase in rotor thrust of 1% will provide a potential payload increase of about 3%, because of the rough proportionality described above. Another source of improved operational performance would be to reduce the engine weight and fuel consumption for a given power. Due, in the main, to increases in allowable engine operating temperatures and improvements in component efficiencies, the weight per unit power and the fuel consumption per unit power have both fallen over recent years. The trend in these quantities, together with a reasonable extrapolation up to the year 2000, is shown in Figure 8.1.

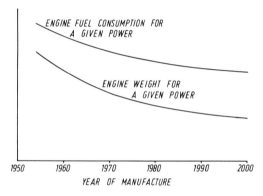

Fig. 8.1 Trends in engine fuel consumption and weight for a given power

In the case of helicopter structures, some significant improvements can be expected in terms of strength and weight with the use of larger proportions of non-metallic and composite materials. The initial use of these materials was limited to the manufacture of lightly loaded panels, where absolute strength is less important than resistance to buckling. Such resistance is mainly provided by thickness, and this is a good application for structural parts made of glass fibre impregnated with epoxy resin, or for honeycomb sandwich materials which are exceedingly stiff and yet very light. But when new fibres, particularly carbon and Kevlar, which were even lighter and had better stiffness characteristics than glass fibre, arrived, the advantages were quickly appreciated.

These materials are very light, have longer fatigue life, require less maintenance and, most important, they can be moulded into complex and highly efficient aerodynamic shapes which cannot be manufactured from conventional metals. A good example is the sketch of a prototype main rotor blade at Figure 8.2. This shape was developed during the British Experimental Rotor Programme (BERP) and is claimed to increase rotor efficiency by up to 40%. Such a complicated shape, in which both cross-sectional and planform shape vary with radius, would be quite impracticable to make from metal. It was largely the benefits conferred by these advanced blades that enabled Westland to raise the world absolute speed

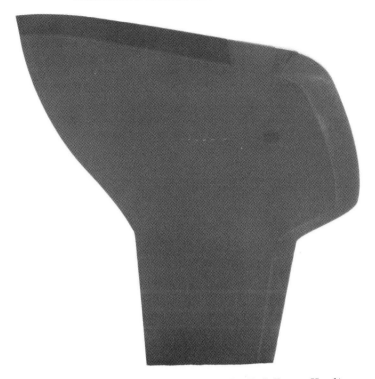

FIG. 8.2 A BERP main rotor blade (*E. J. Everett-Heath*)

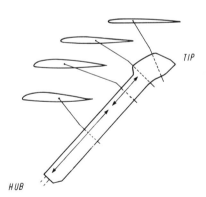

FIG. 8.3 The pre-production ASP blade on an EH-101

record for helicopters to 400.87 kph (249.1 mph) on 11 August 1986 using a modified *Lynx* fitted with BERP blades. After further experimentation and modification to improve hover performance, these blades are now in production for variants of the *Lynx* and the EH-101. Although it may be difficult to get away from the well-known 'BERP', the production blades are actually called ASP – advanced section and planform – blades.

Rotor blades were the first major component to use this new technology, with the initial purpose of increasing fatigue life. However, the possibility, by laying up

FIG. 8.4 The Sikorsky/US Army S-75 ACAP demonstrator (*Sikorsky*)

fibres in particular directions, of tailoring the strength and stiffness of a structural element to the loading it will have to withstand was quickly utilised. It is this ability to tailor strength and stiffness which has made possible future developments like the X-wing discussed later.

Radomes are another common area for non-metallic materials since glass fibre and other similar composites can be made almost transparent to radio waves. This suggests that another potential advantage of these materials is that their use would reduce the radar signature of the helicopter and therefore, by making it more difficult to detect, enhance its survivability. Both Bell and Sikorsky have flown helicopters with an all-composite, non-metallic fuselage under a programme funded by the US Army and known as the Advanced Composite Airframe Programme (ACAP). The programme aims were to construct a helicopter that would allow the occupants to survive a vertical impact at 12.9 m/s (42 ft/s) while making a weight saving of 22% compared with an equivalent metal aircraft and to achieve a 17% reduction in cost. In fact the Sikorsky helicopter achieved savings of 23% in weight and 24% in cost. The aircraft is shown in flight in Figure 8.4.

Of even greater importance for a battlefield vehicle, however, is that some non-metallic components can be made resistant to blast and impact damage, i.e., make the helicopter more tolerant to battle damage. When the corrosion resistance of the materials is considered as well, the resulting properties make the increased use of non-metallic materials inevitable. The present trend in the use of composites by one manufacturer is shown in Figure 8.5.

Vibration

The non-uniformity of the velocity distribution along the rotor blades in forward flight necessarily produces periodically fluctuating air loads on the blades as they

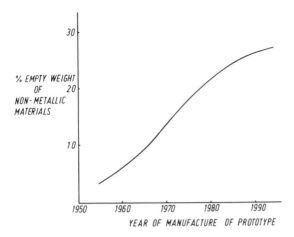

FIG. 8.5 The use of non-metallic materials

rotate. The forces and moments which result from this are at particular frequencies which are dependent upon the rotational speed of the rotor and the number of blades which it contains. Some of these forces are transmitted to the helicopter fuselage and become potent sources of vibration. They may affect parts of the airframe, the flight instruments, the avionics, the crew and particularly any sighting and surveillance devices which the helicopter may be carrying. Indeed, it is often the onset of high vibration levels which limits the useful forward speed of present-day helicopters. The trend towards elastomeric bearings and composite blade materials is helpful here, since the increased damping of these materials helps to reduce the amplitude of these vibrations. In addition to this, much effort is currently being devoted to reducing helicopter vibration levels by means such as special rotor mountings and pendulum-type absorbers. Another technique currently being pursued for vibration reduction is known as higher harmonic control (HHC). In this system, the pitch of the blades is varied continuously under computer control to remove the more significant of the periodically fluctuating air loads. The reduced vibration levels attained by any of these means will also increase helicopter reliability and reduce the maintenance effort required to keep them flying.

NOTAR

A development being pursued by McDonnell Douglas is the NOTAR, i.e., *NO TAil Rotor* aircraft. This does not use a tail rotor for yaw control and torque reaction and therefore does not suffer from the problems discussed in Chapter 3. It uses instead a combination of an aerodynamic phenomenon called the Coanda effect and a controllable nozzle.

It is in the hover that the largest power requirements are made on the tail rotor. As indicated in Chapter 3, in forward flight the power required is reduced at first; at higher forward speeds it rises again to the same levels as in the hover, but at high speeds some aerodynamic side force can be generated by the vertical fin on the aircraft and this can be used to react to the torque.

In the hover, the air is flowing vertically downwards through the rotor as shown in Figure 8.6.

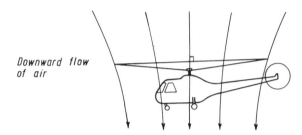

FIG. 8.6 Down flow through the helicopter rotor in the hover

This air flows around the tail boom of the aircraft. In a NOTAR helicopter, air is discharged from tangential slots along one side of the boom. Because of the Coanda effect, this causes the airflow to flow further round the circular cross-section boom on one side than the other. The airflow around the boom therefore curves as shown in Figure 8.7 and this produces a side force acting on the boom, which in turn generates a moment to react to the main rotor torque. Yaw control is provided by a controllable nozzle producing a jet of air at the aft end of the tailboom. Both the air needed for the tangential blowing and for the tail jet nozzle are provided by a fan within the tailboom of the aircraft. An experimental helicopter fitted with the NOTAR device is shown in Figure 8.8. The McDonnell Douglas MD520N/MD530N will be the world's first NOTAR production helicopters; the MD530N flew for the first time in December 1989.

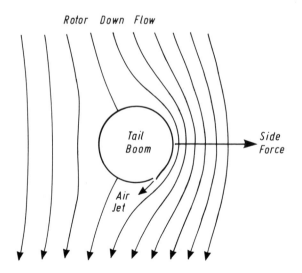

FIG. 8.7 The production of side force by the Coanda effect

FIG. 8.8 A helicopter fitted with the NOTAR device (*McDonnell Douglas*)

The ABC Rotor

All of the ideas described so far, while they can significantly improve the performance of existing machines, do not offer dramatic, overall performance gains. One configuration which does is the advancing blade concept (ABC) from Sikorsky. In this case, there are two separate, rigid rotors, rotating in opposite directions, about a common axis. Roll balance is achieved here by developing lift only on the advancing side of each disc, as shown in Figure 8.9.

Since the advancing blades speed up as the helicopter accelerates, the available lift increases markedly with speed. It is also now feasible to slow the rotor below the optimum tip speed of Figure 3.20 because lift is not required from the

ABC Rotor lift distribution

FIG. 8.9 The lift distribution on the rotors of the ABC aircraft

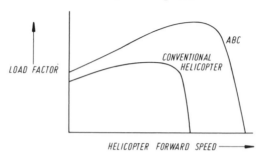

FIG. 8.10 The comparison of load factor on ABC and conventional helicopters

FIG. 8.11 The ABC demonstrator vehicle in flight (*Sikorsky*)

retreating blades. The absence of a flapping hinge, thereby inhibiting downward blade flapping, makes this acceptable. The effect of this is to increase the maximum obtainable forward speed as well. The performance of this configuration compared with a conventional helicopter is indicated in Figure 8.10 and the flight demonstrator vehicle is shown in Figure 8.11.

Another advantage of this layout is that, because of the possibility of controlling the yawing of the aircraft by putting different amounts of power into the two rotors, there is no need for a separate tail rotor. There is therefore both a power saving and a potential reduction in vehicle length. The latter is illustrated in Figure 8.12, which shows an ABC aircraft configured for the American LHX programme. Once again, the removal of the dangerous, and vulnerable, tail rotor is a significant advantage in its own right.

The ABC rotor, while it offers the possibility of increased forward speed through the ability to use lower tip speeds, still has a substantially lower forward speed capability than a fixed-wing aircraft, because of the speed additive effects on the advancing blade. They are, in fact, moving faster than the vehicle itself, and indeed, faster than is really required to generate lift at high forward speeds. The

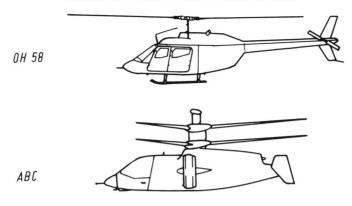

OH 58

ABC

FIG. 8.12 The reduced length of ABC

consequence of this is that they also generate a large amount of drag compared with the fixed wings on a conventional aircraft.

The Tilt Rotor

This disadvantage can be circumvented by using a tilt-rotor. This utilises a rotor in the horizontal plane for take-off and landing, just like a helicopter, but for high speed forward flight, the plane of the rotor is tilted forward, to become, in effect, a large propeller. This configuration offers aircraft manoeuvrability and forward flight speeds up to about 585 kph (365 mph) together with a significant improvement in cruise efficiency. Figure 8.13 indicates the kind of performance that can be expected from this type of vehicle.

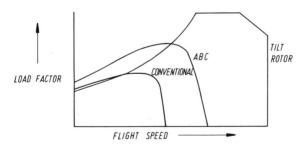

FIG. 8.13 A comparison of load factors

Flight tests on a prototype tilt rotor aircraft, the XV-15, indicated that the transition from rotor-borne to wing-borne flight can easily be achieved over a wide speed range. The constraints of transition are not therefore likely to impose serious operational limitations.

The first production tilt-rotor aircraft should have been, and may still be, the Bell/Boeing V-22 *Osprey*. Its maiden flight took place on 19 March 1989 but within two months of this the Pentagon cancelled the programme. At the time of writing

FIG. 8.14 The V-22 *Osprey* (*Bell*)

uncertainty surrounds the programme but it may continue in one form or another. Delivery of production aircraft to the Services was scheduled to start in 1992. The V-22, which offers fixed-wing performance with an efficient V/STOL capability, has been ordered in considerable numbers by the US Marine Corps, Navy and Air Force. The US Marine Corps requirement for the V-22 is to carry 24 combat-equipped troops at a cruise speed of 463 kph (288 mph) over an operational radius of 370 km (230 miles). It is a sizeable aircraft, having a span from one rotor tip to the other of 26 m (85 ft), a maximum all-up-mass of 26,762 kg (59,000 lb) and a payload of 10,000 kg (22,046 lb). Unrefuelled ferry range is 3,892 km (2,418 miles). The V-22 is an aircraft with an all-composite airframe and it represents a significant step forward in production techniques and in aircraft performance.

The X-Wing

Another concept which is currently under development by Sikorsky is the X-wing. This also relies on the Coanda effect for rotor-borne flight. At low forward speeds the aircraft is basically a helicopter supported by a mechanically-driven rigid rotor. The cyclic variation of lift is provided by varying the quantity of air blown from a tangential slot in the trailing edge of the blades. This blowing causes the air flow around the blade to curve and thereby generate lift on the blade, which is proportional to the blade forward speed and the amount of blowing.

As the forward speed of the vehicle increases, however, the reversed flow region on the retreating side of the disc shown in Figure 3.8 becomes larger. It will be remembered that, in this region, the flow over the blade is backwards, that is, from trailing edge to leading edge. For a normal helicopter blade this produces negative lift, because the blade incidence for this flow direction is necessarily negative in order for the blade further out (where the flow is in the proper sense) to be at the positive incidence needed to generate lift. On the X-wing there are blowing slots at both the leading and the trailing edge of the blades. For higher speed forward flight, air is blown from what is the nominal leading edge of the blade in the reversed flow region. Since the blade is not physically altered in cyclic pitch as it rotates, this blowing also generates positive lift.

Avionics Technology

The complexity of the future military helicopter's task, its sensors and weapons seem set to increase the importance of avionics technology and, in particular, the integration aspects of data fusion and display. The drive to reduce the size of the helicopter and its crew, while expanding its roles and increasing its performance, will result in greater crew dependence upon avionic systems and sub-systems and greater authority for these in the operation of the aircraft. There are a number of well defined areas of advanced technology which offer considerable benefits to both designer and crew.

Active Control Technology (ACT)

The steady increase in both the capacity and the speed of microprocessors should allow the computer to play a larger part in determining the flying qualities of the helicopter than hitherto. Current flight control computers can do little more than make minor changes to the flying characteristics of the helicopter, to make it easier to operate. The computer of an ACT aircraft will totally separate the pilot from the control surfaces. The pilot will use his controls to demand a particular manoeuvre and the relevant signals will pass directly to the computer, which in turn will pass to the control actuators the signals needed to produce precisely that manoeuvre. In this way the designer can provide the pilot with any flying qualities that he wishes, with the result that many of the less desirable flying characteristics of the helicopter, for instance, its slow initial response to control inputs and its lack of dynamic stability in both pitch and roll sensors, can be overcome. This offers the possibility of providing the helicopter pilot with stability and handling qualities more appropriate to a fixed-wing aircraft, with all the associated benefits of reduced workload. However, as the computer system needs to exercise the full authority of the flight controls to achieve its task, system failure would be catastrophic. A triple or quadruple system, using dissimilar hardware and software will be needed to provide the necessary reliability. This type of system is already available on fixed-wing aircraft such as the Airbus A320.

Side Arm Controls

With the development of entirely electronically-signalled flying controls, the need for large control sticks with large moment arms to cope with high control forces, has diminished. Smaller control sticks, mounted on the side consoles rather than the centre of the cockpit, are now possible. These controllers, or inceptors as they are sometimes called, can generate control signals by movement as in a traditional displacement control, or by force sensing, where the pilot applies a force rather than movement to the stick in the direction required. However, pilot incapacitation presents problems in that a centrally-mounted control can be used by either hand whilst one mounted to one side is more difficult to reach and manipulate with the other hand should the pilot be wounded. This is a significant disadvantage for single-pilot helicopters but is less important where two pilots are carried.

Active Vibration Control

Vibration is a fundamental problem in the helicopter, where the rotation of main and tail rotor systems impart some form of cyclical influence on fuselage, crew, systems and passengers. Various mechanical devices have been used to attenuate vibration effects but all have suffered from the weakness that their effect cannot be changed to suit variations in aircraft weight, manoeuvre, system failure or aircraft damage.

With very high speed integrated circuit (VHSIC) development, it is now possible to counter the vibration that has been fed into the fuselage. First accelerometers are fitted to the main rotor gearbox. These signals can then be fed to a microprocessor, their amplitude, frequency and phase determined and an equal and opposite signal generated. This anti-phase signal can then be fed to small actuators situated in the gearbox mountings, to impart an equal and opposite vibration to that being generated by the rotor. In this way any vibration can be countered immediately and with great precision.

Direct Voice Input

Direct voice input offers the opportunity to give voice instructions to aircraft systems, bypassing the time-consuming task of identifying systems switches and making appropriate selections. It also allows crew members to view the outside world rather than the cockpit interior, when giving these instructions. The system consists of a computer loaded with appropriate voice patterns in the form of digital frequency analysed vowels, consonants and numbers, together with some form of visual display. The pilot alerts the computer to the transmission of a message by pressing a cue button on one of his flying controls and then issues an instruction verbally over the intercom. This message is received by the computer, its constituent parts compared with the stored voice patterns and the interpreted data displayed to the crew. If these data are correct the pilot can then authorise the computer to take the action specified in his message with the statement 'OK' or something similar.

The voice recognised may be speaker-dependent or independent. If the independent system is needed, the wide range of voices likely to be experienced by the system leads to a marked limitation in the number of words that can be recognised. A speaker-dependent arrangement is more practicable, with the computer being cassette-loaded prior to each sortie with the voice patterns of all relevant commands from that crew. In this way well over 1,000 words can be recognised by current systems, with a success rate in identification of some 85%.

FIG. 8.15 The instrument panel of a Royal Navy *Commando* Mk 2 (*Westland Helicopters*)

Laser Communications

With the development of the tactical potential of the armed or attack helicopter comes the need to reduce communication signatures of both surveillance and anti-tank aircraft. Any form of communication between these helicopters during the preparation of an attack on an enemy armoured formation could provide warning to the proposed target. The need for completely secure communications between aircraft that are visible to each other, supports the use of a laser communications system which cannot be intercepted unless the receiver is being illuminated by the very narrow beam of laser light.

A laser beam has the added advantage of carrying a wider range and larger volume of information than a radio signal, albeit over a relatively short range even in moderate or good visibility. However in an environment where short-range, line-of-sight communications are an essential part of a helicopter's tactical operations, laser-based communications systems have much to offer.

Global Positioning System (GPS)

Navigation by reference to orbiting satellites has existed for some time in naval vessels but a GPS extends the benefits to all ground vehicles and aircraft. A constellation of some 18 orbiting satellites is to be established as part of the NASA space programme. Any helicopter carrying the relevant receiver will be in view of four of these satellites at all times. Three of them will pass direction information to the navigation receiver and computer in the aircraft, the fourth providing an accurate time signal to allow the navigation and speed data to be synchronised. The accuracy of this system is likely to be within 16 m (52 ft) of true position and 0.1 m per second in measured velocity.

Future Battlefield Use

Of all battlefield vehicles and weapons systems, the helicopter has enjoyed perhaps the most rapid improvements since the Second World War. The more advanced types can lift substantial loads or fight alongside ground troops effectively by day and night, in most weather conditions. Imaginative use of these flexible, lethal machines gives commanders an added potential to influence the outcome of any battle. To realise this, however, commanders must be air-minded and be able to recognise the characteristics and shortcomings of the helicopter, no matter how advanced in design it may be.

9.

Attack Helicopters

The type of helicopter that seems to generate the most interest and the one that more and more countries are procuring is the attack helicopter, perhaps because of its flight performance, firepower, menace and in some cases ugliness! In the view of the Americans and Russians, at least, it is now joining the tank and infantry fighting vehicle as the third basic weapon system of combined arms combat and it has already proved itself in various actions around the world. Such is the attack helicopter's potential that new concepts of employment are being developed for it and therefore some knowledge of its evolution and exponents is necessary.

Over twenty years after the introduction of the first, only four genuine types of attack helicopter have been put into production and all are still in service today: the American AH-1 *Cobra* and AH-64 *Apache*, the Italian A-129 *Mangusta* and the Soviet Mi-24 *Hind*. Old or new, their capabilities are forever increasing as they are updated to incorporate new technologies.

The *Cobra* was the first, setting an example for all the others to follow, with a tandem seating arrangement whereby the pilot sat above and behind the co-pilot/ gunner. All four have wings from which to hang some of their weapons. But from there the *Cobra*'s successors have diverged. The *Cobra* has skids, the others wheeled landing gear, the Western helicopters having a fixed gear and tail wheels, the *Hind* with retractable gear and a nose wheel; the US Army *Cobra* has one engine, the others two; the Western helicopters are dedicated attack helicopters with only two seats, while the *Hind* has a cabin for troops as well; the Western helicopters have their sights in the nose, the *Hind* under it; weapons vary from gun calibres to type of missile guidance to the carriage of bombs by the *Hind*.

The Cobra

The first dedicated attack helicopter to enter production made its maiden flight on 7 September 1965. It was the Bell Model 209, dubbed by the US Army the AH-1G *HueyCobra*, and it was a Private Venture that went gloriously right! Another attack helicopter, the Lockheed AH-56 *Cheyenne*, was already under development but it would be some years before it would be available. As the War in Vietnam intensified it became clear that the US Army could not wait and that an interim helicopter was needed without delay. Bell's decision to proceed was seen to be an inspired one when, on 13 April 1966, 110 production aircraft were ordered and by October 1968 that total had risen to 838.

Because time was of the essence the *Cobra* was based largely on the transmission, two-bladed main rotor system and 1,100 shp Lycoming T53-L-11 engine of the Bell UH-1C. Incorporating the standard UH-1 airframe, this model was actually being employed in Vietnam as a *gunship* (to use the American colloquial term). However, the *Cobra* certainly did not look like the UH-1C. It had a completely new fuselage, only 0.965 m (3 ft 2 in) wide, with no cabin and the two crew seats in tandem. The co-pilot/gunner sat in front, the pilot above and behind him. Both had an excellent all-round field of view. Another innovation was the installation of wings, not only to offload the main rotor in forward flight but also to provide four pylons on which to hang weapons.

FIG. 9.1 The AH-1G *Cobra* (*Bell*)

Various armament options were available. The most common were four pods containing nineteen 70-mm unguided rockets each or two rocket pods on the outer pylons and two six-barrelled 7.62-mm Miniguns in pods on the inner pylons. Later in the War a six-barrelled 20-mm cannon was sometimes fitted on the inner pylon of the port wing. Under the nose was a turret which could house two more Miniguns or two 40-mm grenade launchers or one of each.

This devastating firepower had a significant impact on the fighting and, with the *Cobra*'s good flight performance, ensured the aircraft's success in Vietnam. The termination of the *Cheyenne* project in 1972, however, had led to the start of a new attack helicopter competition that was to result in the AH-64 *Apache*. In the meantime the American withdrawal from Vietnam in the early 1970s had initiated renewed thoughts on the armoured threat in Europe: until the *Apache* entered service in the 1980s the *Cobra* would have to fill the gap. Its armaments, however, were inadequate for the European theatre. An anti-tank guided missile was obviously needed.

The TOW missile was selected and with it a telescopic sight unit to go in the nose. This sight has two settings, a $\times 2$ magnification with a field of view of 30° and a $\times 13$ magnification with a field of view of 4.6°; it can be rotated 110° left and right, up 20.5° and 50° down. Converted from the G model, the new variant was designated the AH-1Q and 101 were ordered. This model could carry eight missiles on the outer pylons, rockets or guns on the inner and it retained the gun turret. The AH-1Q therefore could take on point or area targets, hard or soft, with equal facility. In the event it proved to be underpowered and unsatisfactory and only 92 were delivered. The next sub-type was the AH-1R of which only two were built; converted from G models, they were to test a more powerful engine, the 1,800 shp T53-L-703.

There followed the AH-1S, a complex project which involved the conversion of G and Q models and a new-build programme in three progressive stages, each variant incorporating further technical improvements:

Original Designation	Changed To	No. Delivered
AH-1S (Modification)	AH-1S	337
AH-1S (Production)	AH-1P	100
AH-1S (Up Gun or ECAS: Enhanced Cobra Armament System)	AH-1E	98
AH-1S (Modernised)	AH-1F	99

The AH-1F, to which some previous S, P and E models have been upgraded, is a very capable attack helicopter. It is powered by the 1,800 shp engine and has an uprated gearbox and transmission. When compared to the later *Apache* and *Mangusta*, however, the *Cobra*'s flight performance is somewhat pedestrian, its maximum level speed being only 227 kph (141 mph; 123 knots). Features to reduce vulnerability include modifications to various parts of the helicopter and the fitting of various countermeasures and warning devices. An almost flat plate cockpit canopy is installed to reduce glint. New composite main rotor blades are fitted. They offer more or less unlimited life, lower radar and acoustic signatures, and greater battle damage tolerance: immunity to 7.62-mm rounds and a single 12.7-mm round and up to 30 minutes of flight after suffering a single 23-mm strike. The helicopter's IR signature is minimised by means of engine exhaust gas suppressors and the threat from heat-seeking missiles is further reduced by the inclusion of a jammer mounted above the engine cowling and an IR low reflectance paint scheme. A radar warning receiver is installed to alert the crew to threatening weapons-associated radars and a radar jammer to jam them.

The TOW missile has been retained. Under the nose, however, a new universal

FIG. 9.2 A USMC AH-IW equipped with *Hellfire* missiles and a 20 mm cannon
under the nose (*Bell Helicopter Textron*)

turret, able to accommodate either a 20-mm or 30-mm weapon, is installed. In fact,
a three-barrelled 20-mm cannon, capable of traversing through + 110° in azimuth,
50° in depression and 20.5° in elevation, was chosen. The cannon is controlled by
either the pilot or co-pilot/gunner through the use of helmet-mounted sights or by
the gunner through the TOW sight. 750 rounds can be carried and the rate of fire is
about 730 rounds per minute. Very important is the inclusion of an advanced fire
control system. Consequently a digital ballistics computer and an air data sensor
for gun and rocket firing, a head-up display for the pilot, a laser rangefinder and an
airborne laser tracker are installed. The latter unit searches for, acquires and
tracks target-reflected laser energy originating from friendly laser designators;
once lock-on is achieved the TOW missile sight slews to the target. Among other
improvements for the AH-1F are a Doppler navigation system, secure voice
communications, re-designed instrument panels for both crew members and
lighting to allow operations with night vision goggles.

The USMC also operates the *Cobra* but, because a substantial proportion of
flying hours are spent over water, a twin-turbine version was required. The AH-1J
SeaCobra, though with a Twin Pac powerplant, was substantially the same as the
AH-1G. The Twin Pac consisted of two turboshaft engines coupled to a combining
gearbox with a single output shaft. The J model was quickly followed by the AH-1T
with a better dynamic system, a more powerful Twin Pac powerplant, lengthened
fuselage and tailboom, and TOW missiles. In March 1986 the first AH-1W
SuperCobra was delivered to the USMC. It features two General Electric T700-

FIG. 9.3 A twin-engined AH-1W *SuperCobra* (*Bell*)

GE-401 1,690 shp engines, giving a 65% increase in installed power over the AH-1J. This additional power allows the AH-1W to carry a wider variety and greater number of weapons while still meeting flight manoeuvre requirements.

The AH-1W is configured to carry either eight TOW or *Hellfire* anti-tank missiles as well as two AIM-9L *Sidewinder* or *Stinger* air-to-air missiles; in addition, this variant is equipped with the turret-mounted 20-mm cannon with 750 rounds. Up to 76×70-mm or sixteen 127-mm rockets can be carried instead of the anti-tank missiles.

Despite the many improvements that US Army and Marine *Cobras* have undergone more are in the pipeline. The most important for the AH-1F involves target acquisition and engagement in poor visibility and at night. A FLIR is being put into the TOW sight unit and, together with a FLIR missile tracker, power supply and control panel, the whole unit is called the C-NITE. It gives the *Cobra* the capability to fire the TOW 2 at night and through such obscurants as smoke and fog. For the pilot third generation image intensifying goggles have been issued. They offer increased amplification of ambient light, better visual resolution and improved reliability. Blue-green cockpit lighting is being installed to permit the use of these goggles. Target engagement has already been enhanced, first by the Improved TOW and then by the tandem warhead TOW 2A but in the near future a further improvement may be achieved with the overfly top attack TOW 2B. An air-to-air capability is planned with the installation of a modified version of the shoulder-launched *Stinger* missile.

Depending on the outcome of flight tests and funding, the AH-1W may benefit from a new all-composite, four-bladed, bearingless main rotor, first flown on 24 January 1989. This Model 680-type main rotor gives more thrust, less vibration, lower radar and acoustic signatures, improved manoeuvrability and greater ballistic tolerance. This prototype aircraft is called the *SuperCobra* Plus or AH-1 *Viper* by Bell.

The Apache

Work on a *Cheyenne* substitute for the US Army began in 1972. The first phase of a two-phase development programme was to be a competitive fly-off between two types, the Bell YAH-63 and the Hughes (bought by McDonnell Douglas in January 1984) YAH-64. In Phase two the winner was to go into an engineering development programme focusing on the integration of armaments and day/night target acquisition systems. In December 1976 the YAH-64 was declared the winner.

FIG. 9.4 A pair of *Apaches*, each with eight *Hellfire* and 38 × 70-mm rockets
(McDonnell Douglas)

Taking into account the threat from highly mobile armoured and mechanised infantry units in large numbers operating under the protection of equally mobile and effective tactical air defence systems, the new helicopter – initially dubbed the Advanced Attack Helicopter – had to be substantially more capable than the *Cobra*. Its weapons had to be accurate and lethal against all anticipated targets and it had to be able to fly and fight by day and night and in adverse weather; it would have to survive to fly several missions a day; it would have to be reliable and its maintenance requirements simple enough for troops in the field to be able to cope.

A demanding world-wide flight performance profile was set. At 1,220 m (4,000 ft) and 35°C (95°F), using 95% intermediate rate of power and carrying eight *Hellfire* missiles and 320 rounds of 30-mm ammunition, the *Apache* had to be able to:

– Climb vertically at 2.28 m/sec (450 ft/min) from a hover out of ground effect. It actually achieves 7.4 m/sec (1,450 ft/min).
– Cruise at 269 kph (167 mph; 145 knots).
– Remain airborne for one hour and 50 minutes.

In the European theatre the *Apache* had to be able to carry sixteen *Hellfire* missiles and 1,200 rounds of ammunition at 610 m (2,000 ft) at 21°C (70°F). Exceeding these performance specifications, it can climb vertically from a hover out of ground effect at 5 m/sec (990 ft/min), cruise at 274 kph (170 mph; 148 knots) and it has an endurance of two and a half hours.

Perhaps the best measurement of helicopter manoeuvre performance is vertical rate of climb. But in all respects of manoeuvrability and agility (see Chapter 7) the *Apache* would have to set new standards. The powerplants were the key. Besides providing the performance demanded at 1,220 m at 35°C they also had to meet weight, reliability and maintainability requirements. The two General Electric T700-GE-701 turboshaft engines, now installed, are rated at 1,696 shp each for 30 minutes and 1,510 shp for continuous operation; they are able to provide 1,723 shp automatically as a maximum contingency rating for $2\frac{1}{2}$ minutes when one engine fails. Under most conditions the *Apache* can hover with one engine out of action. The engine control and checking system eliminates the need for constant monitoring of engine instruments, thus allowing the pilot to 'set them and forget them'.

A healthy margin of excess power is available and thus the *Apache* has a lively performance in all flight regimes. At sea level in ISA conditions maximum level cruise speed is 297 kph (185 mph; 160 knots) and in the dive 365 kph (227 mph; 197 knots); 83 kph (52 mph; 45 knots) can be achieved going sideways and backwards. The manoeuvre envelope of $+3.5$ G to -0.5 G allows very rapid changes in the flight path, so vital at very low level and when engaged in air combat, without overloading the airframe structure. Handling qualities are superb and substantially better than those of the *Cobra* with a crisp response to movements of the controls, positive yaw control and a rate of roll of 130° a second between 222 kph (138 mph; 120 knots) and 259 kph (161 mph; 140 knots). The digital automatic stabilisation equipment provides stability in forward flight and in the hover as well as enhancing control responses. In air-to-air combat tests the *Apache* has routinely demonstrated the ability to carry out rolls, loops and split S manoeuvres.

Perhaps even more important than its flight performance are the *Apache*'s armaments and target acquisition and weapon aiming systems. Ultimately it is the weapon that destroys the target; therefore, the weapon must be accurate and the ordnance lethal. The platform that carries it to the point of launch is vital but the manner of its movement, agile or comparatively pedestrian, is arguably less important.

The *Apache* is tasked with a variety of missions. The three most important ones in Europe are envisaged as anti-tank when sixteen *Hellfire* missiles are carried, in the covering force with eight missiles and 38 rockets, and the escort of transport helicopters with 76 rockets and no missiles; in all cases the full complement of 1,200 rounds of 30 mm ammunition is taken and the endurance is two and a half hours.

The primary weapon for the *Apache* is the laser-guided *Hellfire*. Weighing some 45 kg (99 lb), it has a 7.7 kg (17 lb) shaped charge, 178-mm (7 in) diameter warhead, 25.4-mm (1 in) larger than that of the TOW. It is supersonic and has a range of at least 5,000 m when locked on to its laser spot before launch and up to 8,000 m when launched first with lock-on following. The *Hellfire*'s launching options are described in Chapter 6.

The US Army has had the 70-mm (2.75 in) unguided rocket in its inventory for over three decades but the system on the *Apache* cannot be compared with the original. The rocket itself has a variety of warheads, one of which dispenses numerous sub-munitions. Various fuses, which can be set in flight to give the desired detonation range, are available. Thanks to the fast-burning motor, the rocket can be fired out to more than 6,000 m. The four articulated wing pylons assist in achieving accuracy at the longer ranges: they are tilted automatically as the range is put into the fire control system. Both the pilot and co-pilot/gunner can fire the rockets which are usually loaded into a 19-round pod. They can be fired singly, in pairs or in fours.

The M230 single-barrelled Chain Gun is the principal area suppression weapon. It is not operated by gas but by a chain powered by an electric motor. Suspended beneath the cockpits it can traverse 110° left and right, 11° in elevation and 60° in depression. Weighing 67 kg (148 lb), it has an air-to-ground range of some 3,000 m and a rate of fire of about 625 rounds per minute, giving nearly two minutes of sustained fire. Normally the co-pilot/gunner fires the gun which is slaved to the TADS with corrections supplied by the fire control computer. In a back-up mode both crew members can fire the weapon using their helmet-mounted sights for aiming. They have only to look at the target for the gun to slew at 120°/sec to the new line of sight. It can also be fired in the fixed forward (stowed) position. NATO interoperability is achieved with the ability to fire Aden and DEFA 30-mm linkless ammunition as well as the American HE dual purpose round.

With the possibility of helicopter combat in the future, various air-to-air missiles have been test-fired from the *Apache*. They include the *Sidewinder*, the

Fig. 9.5 Potential air-to-air missiles for the *Apache* displayed at the Paris Air Show in 1989 (*E. J. Everett-Heath*)

Stinger, the *Sidearm* and the French *Mistral*. The *Starstreak*, which delivers three explosive darts at hypersonic speed, may also be fired in due course.

Whether all these air-to-ground and air-to-air weapons can be brought to bear on the target depends very much on the *Apache*'s aiming systems. The co-pilot/gunner operates the TADS. Because he sits in the front seat and the system is located in the nose he can have a direct view optical sight, the TADS and the eyepiece being linked by an optical relay tube. The co-pilot/gunner also has a day TV, a laser rangefinder and designator, a laser spot tracker and a FLIR. The optical sight has two settings, a × 3.5 magnification with a 18° field of view and a × 16 magnification with a narrow 4° field of view. The whole TADS 'drum' turns 120° left and right at 60° a second, depresses 60° and elevates 30°. With this optical sight, the TV (with fields of view of 4°, 0.9° and 0.45°), FLIR (50°, 10°, 4° and 1.6°) and the laser devices, the *Apache*'s gunner is well equipped to acquire and track targets, fix their range and then engage them by day or night in poor visibility. It might be expected that vibration would affect the TADS picture but in fact it is rock steady.

The PNVS is a comparatively simple system which contains a FLIR able to sweep 90° to left and right at up to 120° a second, 20° up and 45° down. It generates a TV-like image with a 30° by 40° field of view in a helmet-mounted display in front of the pilot's right eye. While the PNVS can penetrate smoke, haze and thin fog, it has little value in heavy rain and thick fog.

Both crew members of the *Apache* wear a special helmet on which is mounted an integrated helmet and display sighting subsystem, known as IHADSS. Infra-red sensors in the cockpits track the position of the crew's helmets and steer the cannon, the TADS and the PNVS to match the head movements of either crewman.

FIG. 9.6 The PNVS is mounted above the TADS (*E. J. Everett-Heath*)

In other words, the cannon, TADS and PNVS 'look' in the same direction as the crew member to whose helmet they are slaved. In front of one eye is a monocle display, a two-dimensional TV-type monochrome picture derived from the PNVS or the TV in the TADS. A symbol generator superimposes for different flight modes and conditions (cruise, hover, pop-up etc) certain data such as speed, attitude, heading, power and aim point symbol upon the picture. Thus the pilot does not have to keep looking down at his instruments when his whole attention is needed to look outside the cockpit as he flies, for example, NOE at night.

The IHADSS presents some physiological problems that take some getting used to. The pilot's IHADSS picture is coming from the PNVS some 1.2 m (4 ft) below and 3 m (10 ft) in front of him. Thus his 'aided' eye is ahead of his 'unaided' eye when on the move; it follows that the fields of view for each eye do not match – an unnatural phenomenon!

An essential element of the package is the fire control computer which absorbs inputs from the Doppler navigator which in turn receives data from the heading-attitude reference system on true heading and pitch and roll attitude, the flight controls, radar altimeter, the sighting systems and other sources. The fire control computer then processes the information and provides an aiming solution in terms of UTM or latitude and longitude co-ordinates. The Doppler navigation system and the air data system above the rotor head provide the necessary ground and airspeed information for accurate navigation and weapons delivery. The MIL.STD 1553 data bus is a key element, linking together sensors and processors.

Targets may be acquired by the co-pilot/gunner, having selected the sensor he wishes to use (optical sight, TV or FLIR) depending on the visibility, by manually directing the TADS with his thumb control; or by directing the TADS using his IHADSS; or by using his laser tracker to detect the energy placed on the target by a remote designator. The co-pilot/gunner may view the TV or FLIR either from a small monitor screen just below the eyepiece or head-down through the optical relay tube; obviously he must be head-down to look through the optical sight. The attention of one crew member can be directed by the other to a target by means of line-of-sight cueing symbols.

With the pilot sitting above and behind the co-pilot/gunner near the aircraft's centre of gravity it would have been impossible to put the sighting systems in the co-pilot/gunner's cockpit roof. They are therefore in the nose which entails exposure of practically the entire helicopter for target acquisition and engagement except when the *Hellfire* is being fired in the indirect mode. Given the ambush tactics practised by the *Apache*, this is a disadvantage. However, the concept of sights located above the mast was little more than a dream during the *Apache* design stage and was not seriously considered.

In the first half of 1989, however, an Airborne Adverse Weather Weapon System (AAWWS) was installed above the mast on an *Apache* for initial tests. It consists of a millimetre wave fire control radar which can quickly detect, locate and prioritise four types of vehicle: tracked, wheeled, air defence and aerial. In addition, a radio frequency warning and direction finder locates targets that are actively emitting. The AAWWS automatically puts up to sixteen located targets into priority in terms of type, range and speed and then hands them down to a new modular radio frequency seeker in the *Hellfire*. The *Apache* is then unmasked, the missile seekers

FIG. 9.7 The AAWWS (*McDonnell Douglas*)

lock-on to their targets, the missiles are fired and the helicopter masks. This active millimetre wave seeker and inertial guidance system, together with the AAWWS, thus gives the *Apache* a true fire and forget capability. Because of its limited range the AAWWS will complement the TADS and not replace it. It represents a significant step forward, allowing use of the *Hellfire* in any weather and obscuration and enhancing helicopter survivability.

The principles of survivability and battleworthiness, already described in Chapter 7, received due attention in the design of the *Apache*. Ultimately the crew must survive any crash and to that end the *Apache* was designed to give the crew a 95% chance of surviving a vertical crash of 12.8 m/s (42 ft/sec), a lateral impact at 9.1 m/s (30 ft/sec) and a forward crash with the nose down at 15° at 18.3 m/s (60 ft/sec). This is a significantly higher standard than offered by the *Cobra*. The aircraft structure, crew seats and landing gear absorb crash loads, the 30-mm Chain Gun is forced safely up into the space between the cockpits and a static rotor mast and strong canopy frame protect the crew in the event of the helicopter rolling over. The fuel system is crash-resistant. Despite all this a plethora of measures is embodied to reduce the chances, first, of being detected, then of being hit and shot down.

Even though the initial operational capability of the *Apache* was achieved as recently as July 1986, funds have already been spent on an upgrading programme, the first phase of which is known as *Longbow*. It is designed to enhance capabilities by improving systems rather than providing more lift, power and weight. The AAWWS is a key element and other important features include an airborne target

FIG. 9.8 The *Apache*'s 'quiet' scissors tail rotor (*E. J. Everett-Heath*)

handover system which involves the coding of target information and its digital burst transmission between aircraft or to ground stations, better cockpit field of view, the Global Positioning System, integrated crew stations and the installation of two *Stinger* missiles on each wing tip. Export customers might be able to choose between General Electric T701C or Rolls-Royce RTM-322 engines.

The *Apache* has also been offered as a naval attack helicopter with a search and track radar, provision for anti-shipping and air-to-air missiles, enough fuel for six hours flying, folding blades and tail, and other modifications.

The Mangusta

The *Cobra* may be regarded as a medium attack helicopter while the *Apache* is a heavy one. The Italian Agusta A-129 *Mangusta* (Mongoose), on the other hand, is light, weighing little more than half the *Apache* at its primary mission weight. Its height, width and length are less than those of both the *Cobra* and the *Apache*. Arguably, the *Mangusta* is too light and small, lacking the punch and toughness necessary for the battlefields anticipated in the 1990s. Nevertheless, it is a helicopter incorporating advanced technology and a sophisticated mission equipment package.

The *Mangusta* project dates back to 1972 when the Italian Army issued a basic

FIG. 9.9. The *Mangusta* armed with TOW missiles and (*Agusta*)

requirement for an anti-tank helicopter and examined the possibility of building a derivative of the multi-role Agusta A-109. From 1973 to 1975 collaborative studies were undertaken with the West Germans but technical and industrial differences put an end to this cooperation. The Italians continued alone, deciding on a specialist helicopter, rather than a modified A-109, in 1977. The following year the project was launched with a formal operational requirement. The official maiden flight on 15 September 1983 marked a new era for the European helicopter industry: the first flight of the first dedicated attack helicopter designed and built in Western Europe. Deliveries to the Italian Army began in 1989.

The primary role for the *Mangusta* was to be anti-tank with area suppression as the secondary role. It had to be able to match the *Apache* in its ability to operate in battlefield conditions but it was to be considerably cheaper. This factor had a decisive effect on the helicopter's size, weight, armaments and equipment; also on the use of composite materials. Primary mission weight was not to exceed 3,700 kg (8,157 lb) and flight performance parameters at 35°C (95°F) and 2,000 m (6,560 ft) included a cruise speed of 250 kph (155 mph; 135 knots), a 10 m/s (1,970 ft/min) vertical rate of climb and a hover out of ground effect ceiling of 3,015 m (9,890 ft). Just as the *Cobra* and *Apache* need to be agile so does the *Mangusta*: below a weight of 3,400 kg (7.496 lb) manoeuvring load limits are +3.5 G to − 0.5 G; above, +2.8 G to +0.5 G. The acceleration requirement of 0–74 kph (46 mph; 40 knots) in five seconds is met comfortably. For a Western combat helicopter, often observing and firing from the hover, the ability to hover with the wind coming from any direction is essential and therefore tail rotor control is an important design factor. The

Italian Army specified a 36°/sec rate of yaw against the direction of torque with no wind.

In considering how to meet the requirements the designers had many things to think about, those involving the basic configuration including:

– one or two engines (a decision which would have a major impact on size, weight and cost).
– what weapons: TOW or HOT? A gun? If so, what calibre?
– landing gear: skids or wheels? If wheels, retractable or fixed? energy absorbing?
– tandem or side-by-side seating?
– night vision equipment.
– location of sighting systems.
– survivability features.

Even at the maximum take-off weight of 4,100 kg (9,039 lb) there is a power margin. The *Mangusta* is powered by two, well-separated, 825 shp Rolls-Royce Gem 2 Mk 1004D turboshafts. Intermediate contingency rating is 881 shp for 60 minutes and the $2\frac{1}{2}$ minute rating is 994 shp; there is even an emergency rating of 1,018 shp for twenty seconds. The *Mangusta* was the first helicopter to fly the Light Helicopter Turbine Engine Company's T800 engine, rated at 1,200 shp. This was on a trial basis, this engine having been chosen to power the next generation of US attack helicopter, the LHX. The T800 is also a contender for the four nation (Italy, Netherlands, Spain, UK) Light Attack Helicopter project for the late 1990s.

The basic mission requirement for the *Mangusta* is to fly 100 km (62 miles) to its combat area carrying eight TOW missiles, remain there for 90 minutes (45 of which are in the hover, thus using greater engine power and more fuel), and then fly back 100 km to base. At the cruise speed of 250 kph this equates to an airborne time of two hours and eighteen minutes; another twenty minutes fuel reserve was required.

Being so much smaller and lighter than the *Apache*, the *Mangusta* naturally has a lighter weapons load and is therefore less effective. The four wing pylons, articulated 2° up and 10° down, are stressed for 300 kg (661 lb) each. The TOW missiles are mounted in a pod of four at the wing tips, leaving the inner pylons free for 7.62-mm, 12.7-mm or 20-mm gun pods or 7-tube 70-mm rocket pods. 19-tube rocket pods can be carried if the TOW missiles are replaced by the 7-tube pods. Instead of eight TOW missiles eight HOT or six *Hellfire* missiles may be installed; for air combat the *Mangusta* can carry *Sidewinder*, *Mistral* or *Stinger* missiles. A traversable turret under the nose for a 12.7-mm machine gun has also been developed – but not so far for the Italian Army.

The missile sight is the same as that in the *Cobra* and is positioned in the nose. For night and adverse weather anti-tank engagements it has a FLIR incorporated. The *Apache*'s TADS was initially considered but was rejected on the grounds of its weight and the fact that it was optimised for that helicopter; a Honeywell mini-FLIR was chosen instead. To assist the pilot to fly at night a small night vision FLIR (the PNVS was also considered) is located above the nose, its picture being presented to both crew members on the monocle of the same IHADSS as in the *Apache*. As with the American helicopter where the pilot looks so does his FLIR.

FIG. 9.10 A TOW missile being launched from a *Mangusta* (*Agusta*)

The symbology required for the particular condition of flight can be superimposed on to the image, thus giving a faithful head-up picture. At the request of the Italian Army provision for a mast-mounted sight has been built-in. If *Hellfire* missiles are to be fired then at the very least a laser spot tracker will have to be installed; it would be more likely, however, that a laser rangefinder and target designator would also be fitted.

Considerable care has been taken with the reduction of the *Mangusta*'s vulnerability, given its constraints of weight and costs, and many of the features described in Chapter 7 are incorporated. In an effort to see before being seen lookout for the pilot and co-pilot is good and the aircraft's small size helps to delay visual and radar detection. It is claimed that the *Mangusta* has complete ballistic tolerance to 12.7-mm strikes and partial tolerance to 23-mm. Crashworthiness, while better than that of the *Cobra*, does not match the *Apache*'s. A 90% chance of crew survival at a vertical rate of descent of 11.1 m/s (2,190 ft/min) and at a horizontal deceleration of 13.1 m/s (2,579 ft/min) is specified. The energy-absorbing wheeled landing gear assists in achieving this standard.

One of the most interesting technical aspects of the *Mangusta* is its integrated multiplex system (IMS). This digital system, compatible with the MIL.STD 1553B databus, is managed by two redundant central computers, each capable of operating the IMS independently. They are backed by two interface systems which pick up outputs from sensors and avionic equipment and transfer them to the main computers for real-time processing. The processed information is presented to the pilot and co-pilot on separate multi-function displays with keyboards to assess the information required. The IMS handles and monitors communications, navigation, flight controls including stabilisation, the fly-by-wire mode and flight director functions, weapon control and firing, engine and fuel system management, electrical, hydraulic and transmission systems management and many other functions. The IMS computer can store up to 100 geographical points and up to 100 pre-set HF, VHF and UHF frequencies. It does much to meet the objective of minimising crew workload during low level combat operations at night and in adverse weather.

It is possible that the *Mangusta* will be further developed to meet the requirement for a Light Attack Helicopter, a project given the name *Tonal* under study by Italy, the Netherlands, Spain and the UK.

The Hind

The only genuine Warsaw Pact attack helicopter in operational service is the Soviet Mi-24 *Hind*, designed by the Mil bureau. It is far bigger and heavier than any of the NATO attack helicopters and this is because of one simple design feature: it has a cabin big enough to accommodate eight combat-equipped troops. The other feature that sets it apart is its retractable undercarriage.

It is probable that design of the *Hind* began at about the same time that the *Cobra* arrived in Vietnam (September 1967). Since then many different variants have appeared in different guises. However, the NATO designation *Hind* refers to them all, including the Mi-25, the export version of the *Hind D*, and the Mi-35, the export version of the *Hind E*. NATO has designated seven sub-types: *Hind A* through to *G*. The *B* model was a prototype and the *C*, built in small numbers, a variant for training. The *A* model entered operational service. It had a gunner in the nose and a pilot and co-pilot sitting side-by-side behind him. It was heavily armed with a 12.7-mm nose gun, and rockets and anti-tank missiles mounted on stub wings. For the first time a Soviet helicopter had been designed from the outset to have integrated weapons and some armour protection. It thus represented a major change in Soviet design practice.

The vast and flat expanses of the European part of the USSR has had a major influence on Soviet battle doctrine, tactics and the design of equipment. There are

FIG. 9.11 The *Hind A* with its side-by-side pilot seating and single-barrelled nose gun

few trees and the terrain offers little concealment. So in this environment, contrary to the NATO approach, speed has to be used instead of stealth. The manoeuvrability and agility of NATO attack helicopters, particularly at low speeds, has already been mentioned. The *Hind* does not compare in this flight regime, being unstable and difficult to fly in the hover and slow to accelerate away from it. Instead, it outmatches the NATO helicopters in sheer speed. Thus the Soviet design philosophy for the *Hind* is in most senses diametrically opposed to that for NATO attack helicopters.

Within a couple of years the *Hind A* had proved itself as a battlefield helicopter and its potential as an attack helicopter had been recognised. Thus, in 1975, a new model, the *Hind D*, entered production. It featured a completely re-designed front fuselage section with two individual cockpits in tandem rather than side-by-side seating. The single-barrelled nose gun was replaced by a four-barrelled 12.7-mm Gatling gun in a traversable turret under the nose; space was available for the storage of 1,470 rounds. There was no change to the other armaments, the four wing pylons usually carrying four 16 or 32-tube 57-mm rocket pods. 250 kg or 500 kg bombs could be carried instead. Each wing end plate had two missile rails for the AT-2 *Swatter* anti-tank missile. The troop cabin was retained.

The *Hind D* remains in service in many countries today but in 1978 the *Hind E* appeared. It differed from its predecessor by having AT-6 *Spiral* missiles instead of the *Swatters*. Two *Spirals* were mounted on a distinctive H-frame on each wing end plate. The *Spiral*, the only known Soviet missile specifically designed for use on helicopters, is a much more capable missile. It is supersonic and has a maximum effective range of at least 5,000 m, 1,000 m more than that of the *Swatter*. It is radio-guided and is launched from a tube. Because of its speed and undoubted manoeuvrability, the *Spiral* probably has an air-to-air capability against hostile helicopters and other slow-flying targets.

Neither the pilot nor the co-pilot/gunner is thought to have any passive night

FIG. 9.12 A *Hind D* displaying two rails for *Swatter* missiles, 57 mm rocket pods and a four-barrelled 12.7-mm gun in a turret under the nose

Fig. 9.13 The distinctive H-frame missile rails on this *Hind E* can be clearly seen

vision equipment. The pilot has a simple reflector sight in his cockpit to fire rockets and the Gatling gun in the fixed forward-firing mode while the gunner has the missile sight on the starboard side of his cockpit and a gun and bomb sight in front of him. The missile sight is gyro-stabilised and almost certainly has magnifications of about ×3 and ×10 for target acquisition and tracking respectively; fields of view are not known. There is no evidence to suggest that this sight contains a laser rangefinder. The ergonomics of the gunner's cockpit are poor when compared to NATO designs. The gunner has to twist the upper part of his body through about 70° to look down through his missile sight and this is neither comfortable nor conducive to accurate target tracking. The sight itself is located under the fuselage which naturally entails exposure of the entire helicopter when engaging targets. For a NATO attack helicopter this would be a decided tactical disadvantage but it is not so for Warsaw Pact *Hinds* which usually employ an attack profile that involves a pull-up to between 50 m (165 ft) and 100 m (330 ft) AGL and then a shallow dive towards the target.

Though with a rate of fire of some 4,000 rounds a minute, the four-barrelled Gatling gun was considered inadequate in Afghanistan. In 1981 the first *Hind* appeared with a twin-barrelled 30-mm cannon mounted on the starboard side of the fuselage instead of the Gatling gun. It was not until 1986, however, that this variant was designated the *Hind F*. With a fixed cannon the helicopter has to be aligned with the target and this might take more time than is available. Other disadvantages include an ammunition load probably reduced to less than 1,000 rounds and a rate of fire that is probably not much more than half that of the Gatling gun. On the credit side, however, is an increase in range to about 2,000 m and much greater lethality.

FIG. 9.14 The *Hind F* has a 30-mm cannon fixed to the starboard side of the
fuselage instead of a turret-mounted Gatling gun

The 57-mm rocket was also deemed insufficiently lethal and lacking in range
and so a 20-tube 80-mm rocket pod was qualified on the *Hind*. Besides rockets and
bombs the *Hind*'s pylons have been seen to mount a 23-mm cannon in a pod, an
anti-personnel mine dispenser, extra *Spiral* missiles or fuel drop tanks. Thus the
Hind E and *F* can be armed to attack specific or area targets that are hard, such as
tanks, or soft, such as wheeled vehicles. It is to be expected that the Russians have
already followed the American example of installing air-to-air missiles, possibly
modified versions of shoulder-launched SAMs, on some of their helicopters.

During the clean-up operations after the explosion at Chernobyl in 1986 another
variant of the *Hind* was revealed. It was the *Hind G* which had claw-like devices on
the wing end plates instead of missiles. The associated missile sight and radio
command guidance pod under the fuselage had been removed. The Gatling gun
and rockets have been retained so the *Hind G* is well able to defend itself while
going about its tasks, presumably radiation monitoring and probably armed
reconnaissance.

The War in Afghanistan gave impetus to the installation of warning devices and
self-protection measures – essential because of the *Hind*'s poor manoeuvrability,
inadequate ballistic tolerance and insufficient armour plating for key areas. The
spectrum of the threat ranged from aged Lee Enfield rifles to, latterly, *Stinger* and
Blowpipe shoulder-launched missiles. No single measure could cope and so a
combination was proposed. A decoy flare dispenser, containing 128 flares, was at
first strapped under the rear end of the tailboom. The flares could only descend and
thus had a limited effectiveness. This dispenser was superseded by two triangular-
shaped ones located on each side of the forward end of the tailboom. These contain
96 flares each which are fired forwards and slightly upwards, thus remaining in
the air longer and blooming nearer the engine exhausts. Film from Afghanistan
indicated that flare release was pre-emptive and not reactive to a missile approach

warning device. Besides the flares *Hind* were equipped with an IR jammer mounted above the rear end of the cabin. Box-like suppressors were placed over the engine exhausts which had the effect of screening the hot parts of the engines and deflecting their exhaust gases upwards into the rotor downwash. No information is available about the crashworthiness aspects of the *Hind*.

The Mi-28 *Havoc* was revealed to the Western public at the 1989 Paris Air Show. It was only a prototype, however, and, according to officials from the Mil bureau, production is not likely to start until 1990 or later. It would therefore be reasonable to expect at least one more variant of the *Hind* to appear – probably equipped with a new anti-tank missile or with an air-to-air missile and the necessary modifications to the avionics and fire control systems. *Hind* production will continue into the 1990s and it will certainly remain in operational service well into the next century.

TABLE 9.1
Characteristics

	AH-1F *Cobra*	AH-64 *Apache*
Engine power	1,800 shp	$2 \times 1,696$ shp
Main rotor diameter	13.41 m (44 ft)	14.63 m (48 ft)
Fuselage length	13.59 m (44 ft 7 in)	15.24 m (50 ft)
Fuselage width	0.99 m (3 ft 3 in)	2.03 m (6 ft 8 in)
Wing span	3.28 m (10 ft 9 in)	5.23 m (17 ft 2 in)
Height (to rotor head)	4.09 m (13 ft 5 in)	3.84 m (12 ft 7 in)
Operating empty weight	2,993 kg (6,598 lb)	4,881 kg (10,760 lb)
Max gross weight	4,535 kg (10,000 lb)	9,525 kg (21,000 lb)
Max level speed	227 kph (141 mph)	297 kph (185 mph)
Range (internal fuel)	507 km (315 mls)	482 km (300 mls)

	A-129 *Mangusta*	Mi-24 *Hind*
Engine power	2×825 shp	$2 \times 2,200$ shp
Main rotor diameter	11.9 m (39 ft $\frac{1}{2}$ in)	17.3 m (56 ft 9 in)
Fuselage length	12.275 m (40 ft $3\frac{1}{4}$ in)	17.5 m (57 ft 5 in)
Fuselage width	0.95 m (3 ft $1\frac{1}{2}$ in)	1.7 m (5 ft 7 in)
Wing span	3.2 m (10 ft 6 in)	6.65 m (21 ft 10 in)
Height (to rotor head)	3.35 m (11 ft)	3.97 m (13 ft 3 in)
Operating empty weight	2,529 kg (5.575 lb)	8,450 kg (18,629 lb)
Max gross weight	4,100 kg (9,039 lb)	11,500 kg (25,353 lb)
Max level speed	259 kph (161 mph)	335 kph (208 mph)
Range (internal fuel)	575 km (357 mls)	450 km (280 mls)

Self Test Questions

QUESTION 1   What are the characteristics that helicopters have that they exploit for tactical purposes?

Answer   ....

....

....

QUESTION 2   List the major limitations from which helicopters suffer.

Answer   ....

....

....

QUESTION 3   What are the main roles of helicopters when in support of the ground forces?

Answer   ....

....

....

QUESTION 4   How can helicopters help with command and control?

Answer   ....

....

....

QUESTION 5   In what way can tactical transport helicopters assist in the armoured battle?

Answer   ....

              ....

              ....

QUESTION 6   What are the main roles of naval helicopters?

Answer   ....

              ....

              ....

CHAPTER 3

QUESTION 1   Why is it advantageous for a hovering helicopter to have a large rotor?

Answer   ....

              ....

              ....

QUESTION 2   Why is 'Hot-High' the critical criterion for hovering performance?

Answer   ....

              ....

              ....

QUESTION 3   How does a helicopter rotor actually generate thrust and why does it need a supply of power to do it?

Answer   ....

              ....

              ....

QUESTION 4   How is hovering thrust controlled by the pilot?

Answer   ....

....

....

QUESTION 5   What are the disadvantages of using a conventional tail rotor?

Answer   ....

....

....

QUESTION 6   What is a swash plate and how does it work?

Answer   ....

....

....

QUESTION 7   What are the three sets of hinges normally present on a helicopter rotor and why are they there?

Answer   ....

....

....

QUESTION 8   Explain why there is a forward speed at which the power required to fly a helicopter is at a minimum.

Answer   ....

....

....

QUESTION 9   What happens to a helicopter which suffers complete engine failure?

Answer   ....

               ....

               ....

QUESTION 10   What limits the forward speed capability of a conventional helicopter?

Answer   ....

               ....

               ....

CHAPTER 4

QUESTION 1   What type of engine is employed in most military helicopters?

Answer   ....

               ....

               ....

QUESTION 2   What is probably its greatest virtue in helicopter installations?

Answer   ....

               ....

               ....

QUESTION 3   Name the three fundamental components of a typical turbo-shaft engine.

Answer   ....

               ....

               ....

QUESTION 4   Name the two distinct variants of the gas turbine engine employed in helicopters.

Answer   ....

              ....

              ....

QUESTION 5   Why does the output shaft of a helicopter engine have to rotate at substantially constant speed?

Answer   ....

              ....

              ....

QUESTION 6   What component is required in the transmission of the *Gazelle* helicopter which is superfluous in the *Lynx*?

Answer   ....

              ....

              ....

QUESTION 7   Why is the free turbine type of engine always employed in a multi-engine helicopter?

Answer   ....

              ....

              ....

QUESTION 8   What feature of construction in some of today's engines leads to improved availability?

Answer   ....

              ....

              ....

QUESTION 9   What is probably the most important power plant characteristic
                from the pilot's point of view?

                Answer   ....

                            ....

                            ....

CHAPTER 5

QUESTION 1   What is meant by 'avionics'?

                Answer   ....

                            ....

                            ....

QUESTION 2   Which gyroscope instruments appear on the instrument panels
                of most modern helicopters?

                Answer   ....

                            ....

                            ....

QUESTION 3   How many types of self-contained navigational aid are cur-
                rently available and what are they?

                Answer   ....

                            ....

                            ....

QUESTION 4   What is the function of an autostabiliser?

                Answer   ....

                            ....

                            ....

QUESTION 5   What is the function of an autopilot?

Answer   ....

....

....

QUESTION 6   What is a databus?

Answer   ....

....

....

CHAPTER 6

QUESTION 1   What are the shortcomings of machine guns when installed on helicopters?

Answer   ....

....

....

QUESTION 2   In what way did the introduction of anti-tank guided weapons affect the design of tanks?

Answer   ....

....

....

QUESTION 3   What does SACLOS stand for and how does this form of guidance work?

Answer   ....

....

....

QUESTION 4   Explain the *Hellfire*'s ripple mode of fire.

Answer   ....

                ....

                ....

QUESTION 5   What are the main problems that may affect a missile launch?

Answer   ....

                ....

                ....

QUESTION 6   What benefits do armed helicopters offer that attack helicopters
                do not?

Answer   ....

                ....

                ....

CHAPTER 7

QUESTION 1   What are the four main objectives for a designer to achieve
                when considering helicopter survivability?

Answer   ....

                ....

                ....

QUESTION 2   What are a helicopter's five distinctive signatures, any one of
                which may betray its presence?

Answer   ....

                ....

                ....

QUESTION 3   What measures can be taken, in the design stage and during
               operations, to minimise the chances of visual detection?

               Answer   ....

                             ....

                             ....

QUESTION 4   Why are helicopters on the ground difficult to conceal?

               Answer   ....

                             ....

                             ....

QUESTION 5   What tactical measures can be taken to reduce vulnerability?

               Answer   ....

                             ....

                             ....

QUESTION 6   In what respects should a combat helicopter be manoeuvrable
               and agile?

               Answer   ....

                             ....

                             ....

QUESTION 7   How may enemy fire up to a given calibre be tolerated?

               Answer   ....

                             ....

                             ....

QUESTION 8   Why is armour used only sparingly?

                Answer   ....

                            ....

                            ....

QUESTION 9   List the ways of preventing post-crash fires.

                Answer   ....

                            ....

                            ....

QUESTION 10   What factors must be assessed when considering the installa-
                tion of any piece of survivability equipment?

                Answer   ....

                            ....

                            ....

CHAPTER 8

QUESTION 1   Why does a 1% increase in hovering efficiency produce a poten-
                tial vertical lift payload increase of about 3%?

                Answer   ....

                            ....

                            ....

QUESTION 2   There are at least six potential advantages in using non-
                metallic materials in battlefield helicopters. What are they?

                Answer   ....

                            ....

                            ....

QUESTION 3   What is the source of helicopter vibration?

                  Answer   ....

                                ....

                                ....

QUESTION 4   What particular problems does vibration in helicopters cause?

                  Answer   ....

                                ....

                                ....

QUESTION 5   Explain the principle of operation of the NOTAR device.

                  Answer   ....

                                ....

                                ....

QUESTION 6   How does the ABC rotor achieve increased manoeuvrability and
                  higher forward speeds than a conventional helicopter?

                  Answer   ....

                                ....

                                ....

QUESTION 7   Explain the principle of operation of the tilt-rotor aircraft.

                  Answer   ....

                                ....

                                ....

QUESTION 8   How does direct voice input work?

                  Answer   ....

                                ....

                                ....

QUESTION 9   What is a sidearm controller?

Answer   ....

                ....

                ....

Answers to Self Test Questions

CHAPTER 2

QUESTION 1   (a)   A comparatively wide speed range.
                       (b)   The ability to hover and make use of the terrain.
                       (c)   Role flexibility.
                       (d)   Good communications.

QUESTION 2   (a)   Lack of ground-based approach and landing aids.
                       (b)   Insufficient anti and de-icing facilities.
                       (c)   Limited endurance.
                       (d)   Vulnerability to enemy fire.

QUESTION 3   (a)   Attack.
                       (b)   Reconnaissance, observation and target acquisition.
                       (c)   Direction of fire.
                       (d)   Command and control.
                       (e)   Tactical support.
                       (f)   Logistic support.

QUESTION 4   (a)   As an airborne command post.
                       (b)   Carrying commanders and staff officers.
                       (c)   Carrying messages during periods of radio silence.
                       (d)   When used as radio relay and rebroadcast stations and as traffic control posts.
                       (e)   Electronic warfare.

QUESTION 5   By deploying infantry anti-tank teams to counter local penetrations.

QUESTION 6   (a)   Anti-submarine warfare.
                       (b)   Anti-surface warfare.
                       (c)   Over-the-horizon targeting.
                       (d)   Airborne early warning.
                       (e)   Tactical support.
                       (f)   Logistic support.

CHAPTER 3

QUESTION 1   The power required to generate thrust for a helicopter rotor
              varies approximately inversely with the rotor diameter. There-
              fore the larger the rotor which can be used, the lower will be the
              power required from the engine to hover. The engine will
              therefore be lighter and less fuel will be required. Hence, in
              turn, the all-up-weight of the helicopter is reduced and there-
              fore less thrust is needed and less power is required.

QUESTION 2   The power required to generate thrust also depends inversely on
              the square root of the air density. The air density falls with
              increasing altitude and with increasing temperature. Hence the
              'Hot-High' criterion.

QUESTION 3   The rotor actually generates thrust because the blades produce
              aerodynamic lift as they rotate. The sum of the lift on all the
              blades equals the thrust of the rotor. The blades also produce
              drag in the plane of the disc. It is the power needed to drive the
              blades against their own drag which the helicopter power plant
              needs to supply in order that the rotor may generate thrust.

QUESTION 4   Hovering thrust is changed by the pilot by altering the pitch of
              all of the blades simultaneously, i.e., collectively. He does this
              by using the collective lever.

QUESTION 5   A conventional tail rotor is very noisy, a danger to personnel
              and is itself easily damaged when the helicopter is close to or on
              the ground. It also creates a lot of drag in high speed forward
              flight.

QUESTION 6   A swash plate is a device for transmitting control inputs from
              the fixed, i.e., non-rotating, body of a helicopter to the rotating
              blades. It consists of two parallel plates separated by a bearing.
              Movement of the lower plate either vertically or by tilting
              causes the upper plate to move with it. Control rods connected to
              the upper plate then produce pitch changes in the rotor blades.
              Vertical movement changes collective pitch; tilting changes
              cyclic pitch – see Figures 3.3 and 3.14.

QUESTION 7   The three sets of hinges normally present on a helicopter rotor
              are:
              (a) Feathering hinges. These allow the pilot to change the
                   pitch of the blades, which he needs to do to control the
                   helicopter.
              (b) Flapping hinges. These allow the blades to flap up and

down as they rotate. This removes the lift imbalance and hence the overturning moment on the helicopter in forward flight.

(c) Lagging hinges. These allow the blades to move in the plane of the disc as they rotate, and so remove the large forces which would otherwise be consequent upon the blade flapping motion.

Note that these hinges may not actually be pin-joints; they can also be flexible metal elements which look quite rigid.

QUESTION 8   There are three contributions to helicopter forward flight power:

(a) Induced power. This reduces rapidly as the helicopter forward speed increases.

(b) Parasite power. This varies as the cube of helicopter forward speed.

(c) Profile power. This increases relatively slowly with forward speed.

The sum of these three components has a pronounced minimum as shown in Figure 3.18.

QUESTION 9   In the event of engine failure, the aircraft will start to descend. As it picks up vertical speed, the upward flow of air can be used to provide lift and the aircraft can glide to earth. It is necessary that it is initially high enough or, if it is initially flying at low altitude, that it is flying fast enough, for it to enter this autorotative state before it reaches the ground, if a controlled landing is to be achieved.

QUESTION 10   The theoretical limit to helicopter forward speed comes from a combination of aerofoil stall at the tip of the retreating blade and compressibility drag rise at the tip of the advancing blade. These effects lead to a loss of lift, a substantial increase in power required and rotor vibration. In many cases it is the onset of very high vibration levels which actually determines the maximum usable forward speed; this is often well below the theoretical speed limit referred to above.

CHAPTER 4

QUESTION 1   The gas turbine is used almost exclusively.

QUESTION 2   It has an excellent power-to-weight ratio, a very important consideration in helicopters.

QUESTION 3   The compressor, combustor and turbine(s) which together provide the net output in the form of a rotating shaft.

QUESTION 4   The single-shaft or fixed turbine engine and the free turbine type.

QUESTION 5   It is important for both mechanical and aerodynamic reasons that the rotor operates at a substantially constant speed. At too high a speed there is a risk of mechanical failure, while at too low a speed the aerodynamic performance of the rotor deteriorates with a risk of the blades coning and therefore sustaining a possible catastrophe.

QUESTION 6   An automatic clutch. In the *Gazelle* the single-shaft engine must be capable of being disconnected from the rotor during start-up. A free turbine gas generator section can be run up while the turbine and rotor are at rest, since there is no mechanical connection.

QUESTION 7   Because at normal power outputs, which are fairly low, the free turbine engine can have a reasonably good fuel consumption while having the ability to provide a high contingency in an emergency.

QUESTION 8   By constructing a modular engine it is relatively straightforward to replace a defective module and rapidly return the engine to service, rather than withdraw the complete unit for repair.

QUESTION 9   The pilot looks for good handling characteristics, i.e., the ability to meet his requirements in a safe, rapid and predictable manner.

CHAPTER 5

QUESTION 1   It is a general term used to describe all the electrical and electronic equipment in a helicopter or aircraft.

QUESTION 2   (a) Artificial horizon (AH).
               (b) Direction indicator (DI).
               (c) Turn and slip indicator.

QUESTION 3   Two. Doppler systems and inertial navigation systems. Doppler is currently preferred for battlefield helicopters.

QUESTION 4   It relieves the pilot of the immediate task of controlling the helicopter. It is a damping device in pitch and roll and also damps out turbulence by using rate gyroscopes and series actuators.

QUESTION 5   It allows specific performance values or data to be held without the need for pilot inputs. It operates in parallel with and separate from the autostabiliser.

QUESTION 6   It is a data transmission system linking sensors, instruments and selectors through a microprocessor. A small number of cables act as a data path for a large number of systems, the information from which is packaged, coded, addressed and then passed down any free channel in the databus, interleaved with other system data, to the receiving instrument or control.

CHAPTER 6

QUESTION 1   They are short-range weapons which require the helicopter to close with the enemy. Space and weight preclude the carriage of many rounds. Ammunition feed and ejection are usually complicated. Airframe distortion, vibration, crosswinds and the speed and attitude of the helicopter all affect accuracy whatever the range and size of the target.

QUESTION 2   Henceforth they required protection against chemical energy weapons in addition to kinetic energy weapons. More parts of the tank required armour protection because helicopters could be expected to fire from different angles compared with ground-based anti-tank weapons.

QUESTION 3   Semi-automatic command to line-of-sight. The gunner has merely to keep the sight's cross-hairs on the target for the missile to hit it.

QUESTION 4   Ripple fire is achieved by using two or more laser designators on different codes. These codes are pre-set in the *Hellfires'* seekers allowing them to be fired in quick succession.

QUESTION 5   Vibration, rotor downwash, helicopter attitude, and wind velocity.

QUESTION 6   Attack helicopters are usually, by definition, two-seat aircraft. Armed helicopters, on the other hand, normally have a cabin and therefore can use it to carry a wide variety of personnel and equipment; weapons can be removed to provide a greater payload although certain fittings are fixed.

CHAPTER 7

QUESTION 1   A helicopter should be:
(a) Difficult to detect.
(b) Difficult to hit.
(c) Difficult to shoot down.
(d) Crashworthy.

QUESTION 2   (a) Visual.
(b) Acoustic.
(c) Radar.
(d) Infra-red.
(e) Electronic.

QUESTION 3   (a) Make the helicopter as small as possible.
(b) Use a paint scheme that blends the helicopter in with its background.
(c) Use matt paint.
(d) Install flat plate canopies.
(e) Keep rotor downwash to a minimum.
(f) Keep out of sight of the enemy for as long as possible; when exposure is inevitable make it as short as possible.

QUESTION 4   (a) Satisfactory measures to prevent ground-based and airborne thermal imaging and other detection devices are not yet in service.
(b) With skids, or even wheels, they are difficult to move into cover.
(c) Particularly because of the main and tail rotors they are difficult to camouflage.

QUESTION 5   (a) Keep exposure to the enemy to a minimum.
(b) Open fire at maximum effective range.
(c) Move, having opened fire and before retaliatory fire arrives.
(d) Operate in conjunction with the ground forces, fixed-wing aircraft and other helicopters.

QUESTION 6   It should have:
(a) Rapid acceleration and deceleration from and to the hover in all dimensions.
(b) The ability to sustain positive G and negative G for a few seconds.
(c) A high rate of roll.
(d) Positive yaw control.
(e) A crisp response to control inputs.

QUESTION 7   By incorporating the following features:
              (a) Armour plating.
              (b) Redundancy.
              (c) Separation.
              (d) Ballistically tolerant materials.
              (e) Fire suppression.

QUESTION 8   Armour is expensive and heavy and reduces the useful payload
              that the helicopter could otherwise carry.

QUESTION 9   (a) Crashworthy fuel tanks.
              (b) Tanks positioned away from ignition sources.
              (c) Breakaway valves.

QUESTION 10   (a) Cost-effectiveness.
              (b) Weight.
              (c) Volume.
              (d) Power consumption.
              (e) Maintenance and logistic requirements.

CHAPTER 8

QUESTION 1   In the hover, the thrust of the helicopter rotor must be identical
              to the total weight of the helicopter. Therefore, a 1% increase in
              hovering thrust will allow the all-up-weight to increase by 1%.
              If everything else remains unchanged, this will appear as a
              relative increase approximately three times larger in the
              payload, which is approximately one-third of the all-up-weight.

QUESTION 2   The potential benefits of non-metallic materials are:
              (a) They may be made lighter for the same strength, par-
                   ticularly in thin-skinned areas.
              (b) They may be made almost transparent to radio waves.
              (c) Their strength, stiffness and shape may be easily
                   tailored for special applications, e.g., rotor blades.
              (d) They can be made resistant to impact and blast damage.
              (e) They are corrosion-resistant.
              (f) They possess high inherent damping, which helps to
                   reduce the effects of vibration.

QUESTION 3   Helicopter vibration is caused by the difference in air speed on
              the advancing and the retreating blade of the rotor in forward
              flight. This produces rapidly changing airloads and hence blade
              vibrations which are transmitted through the rotor hub to the
              helicopter fuselage.

QUESTION 4   Vibration can cause airframe and pilot fatigue, make instruments inoperable or unreadable and render sighting and surveillance devices ineffective.

QUESTION 5   The NOTAR device replaces the conventional tail rotor by a combination of two other mechanisms. The main torque reaction is provided by the sideload generated on the tail boom by tangential blowing in the presence of the down flow from the main rotor. Yaw control is provided by a separate controllable air jet at the tip of the boom.

QUESTION 6   The advancing blade concept achieves roll balance by using the lift on the advancing side only of two co-axial rotors rotating in opposite directions. This increases the lift available since the loss of lift on the retreating side of the disc is no longer a limiting factor on the total lift available nor on the maximum attainable forward speed.

QUESTION 7   The tilt-rotor aircraft uses its rotors in the horizontal plane like a helicopter for low-speed and hovering flight, but tilts them to the vertical for high-speed forward flight. This removes all of the special-to-helicopter speed limitations described, since these are caused by movement of the rotor disc in the same plane as the blade rotation.

QUESTION 8   DVI consists of a data base containing specific words that are to be recognised, a visual display upon which the recognised word is displayed and an audio input from the pilot or crew member. The pilot gives his voice instruction to the voice recogniser, the computer searches its data base for a similar word and displays its result on the visual display. The pilot checks its accuracy before authorising the relevant action by using another specific codeword or pressing a selector switch.

QUESTION 9   A control stick mounted on the side console of the cockpit rather than in its centre. It can operate in a conventional form, being displayed laterally or fore and aft to control aircraft movement, or it can operate entirely on a force sensing basis. It can also incorporate both height and heading control by adding movement in both vertical sense and azimuth.

Glossary of Terms and Abbreviations

A

AAM	Air-to-air missile.
AAWWS	Airborne Adverse Weather Weapon System.
ABC	Advancing blade concept.
ACAP	Advanced composite airframe programme.
ACT	Active control technology.
Aerofoil section	The cross-sectional shape of a surface designed to produce lift and minimise drag.
AEW	Airborne early warning.
AFCS	Automatic flight control system.
Agility	The rate at which a helicopter can accelerate and decelerate in any direction.
AGL	Above ground level
Airmobility	The tactical movement of combat troops, specially trained to go by air, and their airportable equipment as a cohesive force ready to fight.
Air transportability	The transport of troops, equipment and supplies in non-tactical loads to areas short of their combat positions.
Angle of incidence	The acute angle between the chord line and the horizontal or longitudinal axis of the helicopter.
Armed helicopter	A multi-role helicopter with one or more permanent or removable weapons; usually used in a defensive role.
Articulated rotor system	A rotor system in which the blades are free to flap, lag and feather (change pitch) by means of hinges connecting them to the rotor head.
ASI	Airspeed indicator.
ASP	Advanced section and planform.
Assault helicopter	A helicopter, usually but not necessarily armed, which is used to carry troops into combat.
ASUW	Anti-surface warfare.
ASW	Anti-submarine warfare.
ATGW	Anti-tank guided weapon.
Attack helicopter	A helicopter which is specifically designed, in terms of flight performance, integrated weapon systems and survivability features, to fight.
Attitude stabilisation	An AFCS function in which an attitude error signal from a vertical gyroscope is used to improve the helicopter's natural stability.

Autogiro	A rotorcraft driven by a propeller and lifted by a rotor which turns freely in flight under the single influence of the air flowing through the blades.
Autopilot	A long-term datum holding facility associated with one or more functions of the AFCS, employing separate but parallel actuators to hold the set datum.
Autorotation	The free rotation of a rotor resulting from an inflow of air upwards through the rotor disc due to the descent of the helicopter.
Axial flow compressor	A compressor in which the flow of air is parallel to the axis of the shaft.

B

BERP	British experimental rotor programme.
Black hole	A system which rapidly mixes ambient air with the exhaust gases to help to reduce the infra-red signature of the engines.
Blade loading	The ratio of the aircraft's maximum take-off weight to the total blade area.
Blade stall	A blade can stall when on the retreating side of the rotor disc if the helicopter's forward speed is too high; in that event there is a corresponding decrease in relative air-speed and thus lift.

C

CCS	Control communication system.
Centrifugal compressor	A compressor which draws air in at its centre and forces this through radial vanes to exit at its periphery.
Chaff	Dipole reflectors which are dispensed in flight to disguise the radar signature of a helicopter.
Chord	The distance between the leading edge and the trailing edge of an aerofoil section or rotor blade.
Collective pitch	Uniform and simultaneous application of pitch to all the main rotor blades.
Combustor	A chamber in an engine where a mixture of fuel and air is burned.
Coanda effect	The tendency of a flow of air to adhere to a solid surface even though it curves away from the axis of the flow.
Compound helicopter	A helicopter which has either fixed wings or propulsive engines to assist the main rotor system to provide lift and/or propulsion.
Compressor	An aerodynamic rotational device which raises the pressure of the air passing through it.
Coning	Rotor blades are said to cone when, instead of rotating in the horizontal plane passing through the rotor hub, they sweep out the shape of a shallow cone and thus produce an angle between the blades and the horizontal plane.

CRT	Cathode ray tube.
Cyclic pitch	The angle of an individual rotor blade as it meets the relative airflow; it varies as it rotates.

D

Databus	An electronic datapath which uses a small number of cables, down any of which can be passed digital information from numerous sensors or controls, as transmission space is available.
Disposable load	That part of the total operating weight of a helicopter which is available to the user for fuel, payload or role equipment.
Doppler navigation	This is based on the principle of the Doppler effect (or shift) whereby radiation emitted by a moving source is changed in frequency as perceived by an observer who is stationary in relation to the source; the difference between the frequency received and the frequency transmitted by the source is known as the Doppler shift. A Doppler navigation system provides a continuous indication of position by combining forward and lateral speed derived from the measurement of the Doppler effect of the radar signals transmitted to, and reflected back from the ground.
Disymmetry of lift	Unequal lift generated by the main rotor blades as they rotate due to the forward speed of the helicopter.
Drag	The force which opposes motion.
DVI	Direct voice input.

E

Elastomeric bearings	Bearings which consist of alternate layers of metal shims and a rubber-like compound (an elastomer).

F

FADEC	Full authority digital engine control.
FEBA	Forward edge of the battle area.
Feathering hinge	A hinge at the root of a rotor blade about which changes in pitch angle are made.
Fenestron	A tail rotor set within the tail fin, similar to a ducted fan.
FITOW	Further improvements to TOW; a British development of the TOW missile.
Fixed turbine	A turbine which is fixed directly to the output shaft.
Flapping hinge	A hinge at the root of a rotor blade which allows the blade to move up and down freely.
FLIR	Forward looking infra-red.
Fly-by-wire	The passage of flying control commands to the control surface by electronic means.
Free turbine	A turbine which has no mechanical connection to the gas generator.

Fully articulated rotor	A rotor system in which the main rotor blades are free to flap, feather and lag.

G

G	During manoeuvring flight an aircraft experiences increased gravitational weights referred to as g; for example, 0.5 g due to the radial acceleration of the turn plus the static 1 g.
Gas generator	The principal working parts of a gas turbine engine.
GHz	Gigahertz.
GPS	Global positioning system.
Gyroscope	A solid rotating wheel mounted within a ring, the axis being free to turn in any direction.

H

HAC	Hélicoptère anti-char, anti-tank helicopter.
HAP	Hélicoptère d'appui-protection, escort helicopter.
HE	High explosive.
Hellfire	An American anti-armour missile that homes on to a laser spot.
HF	High frequency.
HHC	Higher harmonic control. A computer controlled vibration suppression system.
HOT	Haut subsonique optiquement téléguidée (tiré d'un tube). A French anti-tank missile.
Hot and high	The adverse combination of high altitude and high ambient temperatures.
HQ	Headquarters.
HSI	Horizontal situation indicator.

I

IHADSS	Integrated helmet and display sight system.
IFF	Identification friend or foe.
Induced power	The power required to generate lift.
IMS	Integrated multiplex system.
INS	Inertial navigation system.
IR	Infra-red radiation.
ISA	International standard atmosphere.

K

km	Kilometres.
knots	Nautical miles per hour.
kph	Kilometres per hour.

L

Laser	Light amplification by stimulated emission of radiation.
Lag hinge	A hinge at the root of the rotor blade which allows restricted movement in azimuth.

LHX	Light helicopter experimental.
Lift	The force at right angles to the direction of motion; it overcomes weight and provides a manoeuvre capability.
Load factor	The ratio of lift to weight.

M

M	Metres.
MAD	Magnetic anomaly detector.
Manoeuvrability	The ability to change speed and direction.
Mast-mounted sight	A sight that is mounted directly above the main rotor head.
MFD	Multi-function display.
MIL.STD.	Military standard.
mm	Millimetres.
mph	Miles per hour.
Multiplexing	The coding, addressing and transmission of data down available channels of a databus, between packages of information from either sensors or controls, and their interpretation at destination.

N

NOE	Nap of the earth.
NOTAR	No tail rotor. An aerodynamic yaw control and torque reaction system replaces the tail rotor by a combination of side force on the tail boom and a controllable reaction jet at its tip.

P

PAH	Panzerabwehrhubschrauber; anti-tank helicopter.
Parasite drag	The drag of all the different parts of the helicopter.
Payload	The useful load of a helicopter.
Pitch	The acute angle between the chord line of a rotor blade and the plane of rotation of the main rotor, normal to the rotor shaft.
PNVS	Pilot's night vision sensor.
Precession	The angular change of the plane of rotation of a gyroscope under the action of an applied moment.
Pressure (pitot) head	A device which feeds static and dynamic pressure to certain flight instruments.
Profile power	The power required to turn the rotor against the drag of its blades.

R

Rate gyroscope	A two-way frame gyroscope with freedom about its spinning axis and about an axis perpendicular to the spinning axis, which is restrained by springs.
Rate stabilisation	An AFCS function where the error signal from a rate

	gyroscope is used to improve the aircraft's natural stability.
Redundancy	Aircraft systems which are duplicated or even triplicated, usually for purposes of reliability or survivability.
Rigid rotor	A main rotor system in which the blades do not have hinges; also known as a bearingless rotor.
RMI	Radio magnetic indicator.
Rotor downwash	The air forced downwards as a result of the rotation of the blades.
rpm	Revolutions per minute.

S

SACLOS	Semi-automatic command to line-of-sight.
SAM	Surface-to-air missile.
SAR	Search and rescue.
SAS	Stability augmentation system.
Semi-rigid rotor	A main rotor system in which the blades have only a feathering hinge.
shp	Shaft horsepower.
Sidearm control	A single force feel control which performs all the functions of conventional helicopter controls.
Skin friction	Friction which is generated when relative motion exists between a body and the air.
Specific fuel consumption (sfc)	An air-breathing engine performance parameter defined as fuel flow rate divided by net thrust.
Spiral	The NATO name for the Soviet AT-6 anti-armour missile specifically designed for helicopters.
Split S	A manoeuvre whereby the helicopter is rolled left or right to the inverted position and then pulled through the half loop remaining back to the normal flight attitude.
Stalling angle	At incidence angles greater than the stalling angle an aerofoil section loses lift and shows a sharp increase in drag. The aerofoil is then said to have stalled and the aircraft loses height.
Swash plate	The device on the rotor shaft which permits pitch changes to be made to the rotor blades.
Swept tip	The angling rearwards of the tip section of a rotor blade or wing.

T

TADS	Target acquisition and designation sight.
Tail rotor	A small rotor, nominally in the vertical plane, which reacts to the main rotor torque and provides control in yaw.
TANS	Tactical air navigation system.
TAS	True air speed.
Thermal imaging	All objects emit energy depending on their temperature

	and those that radiate differently from their surroundings present a thermal contrast which can be detected and displayed as an image.
Thermodynamic efficiency	The ratio of energy output of an engine to the energy content of the fuel.
Torque	The twisting moment associated with the transmission of power in rotating mechanisms.
Total rotor thrust	The force produced by the main rotor at 90° to its plane of rotation.
TOW	Tube-launched, Optically-tracked, Wire-guided. An American anti-tank missile used by the British *Lynx* helicopter among others.
Transmission	Gears by which power is transmitted from the engine(s) to the main and tail rotors.
TRIGAT	A third generation, anti-tank missile being developed jointly by Britain, France and West Germany.
Turbine	A device which extracts energy from a flow of gas to provide a power output.
Turboshaft engine	A gas turbine engine which produces power through a rotating output shaft.
U	
UHF	Ultra high frequency.
USMC	United States Marine Corps.
UTM	Universal Transverse Mercator.
V	
VHF (AM)	Very high frequency (amplitude modulated).
VHF (FM)	Very high frequency (frequency modulated).
VSI	Vertical speed indicator.
Y	
Yaw	The motion around the normal axis. This passes through the centre of gravity and is vertical when the aircraft is flying straight and level.

Bibliography

EVERETT-HEATH, E. J., *British Military Helicopters,* Arms and Armour Press, London, 1986.
FAY, J., *The Helicopter and How It Flies,* David and Charles, Newton Abbot.
MUNSON, K., *Helicopters and other Rotorcraft Since 1907,* Blandford Press, London, 1973.
ROYAL MILITARY COLLEGE OF SCIENCE, *The Aerodynamics of Low Speed Aircraft and Helicopters.*
TAYLOR, M. J., *History of Helicopters*, Hamlyn, London, 1984.

Index

Army Air Corps   12, 69
Air-to-air missiles   86, 87, 132, 141, 143, 144
AAWWS   90, 134, 135
Achenbach   3
Acoustic signature   95, 97, 127, 129
Active control technology   121
Aérospatiale   31
AF 532 sight   14, 15
AFCS   38, 62, 70
Afghanistan   10, 11, 103, 142, 143
Air assault   17
Airborne early warning   19, 22
Algeria   6, 8, 77
Anti-icing   11, 75
Armour plating   93, 105, 106, 143
ASP   98, 113
ASUW   20
ASW   19, 20, 99
Attack helicopter   9, 12, 14, 17, 87, 88, 90, 91,
    108, 125, 126, 136, 138, 140, 141, 142
Autogiro   4, 5, 6, 41
  C–4, Cierva   5
  C–6C, Cierva   5
  C–8L Mk 2, Cierva   5
Autopilot   61, 62, 70
Autorotation   4, 6, 41

Battle damage   108, 114, 127
Bell Helicopters   114, 125, 129
BERP   112, 123
Bienvenu   1
Bombs   12, 85, 87, 125, 141, 142, 143

Casualty evacuation   6, 17, 23, 88
Cayley, Sir George   1
Central communications system   69
Chaff   101, 103
Chain Gun, M230   132
Chernobyl   143
Cierva, Juan de la   4, 5, 6, 34
C-NITE   129
Coanda effect   115, 116, 120
Command and control   16, 17, 88, 108
Cornu, Paul   2
Crashworthiness   93, 107, 108, 135, 139, 144
Crocco, G.A.   3

CRT   65, 67, 74, 75, 90
Cyprus   6

Databus   59, 60, 134, 139
da Vinci, Leonardo   1
Decca   70
Direction of fire   5, 15, 16
Direct voice input   122
Doppler   61, 69, 70, 98, 99, 102, 128, 134

Elastomeric bearings   39, 115
Electronic signature   95
Ellehammer, Jakob   3
Engines
  Antoinette   2
  Astazou, Turbomeca   51
  Gem, Rolls-Royce   52, 53, 54, 56, 138
  Gnome, Rolls-Royce   52
  Lycoming   126
  RTM–322, Rolls-Royce/Turbomeca   57, 58,
    136
  T700, General Electric   128, 131, 136
  T800, LHTEC   138
  Turbo, Turbomeca   55
  Twin Pac, Pratt & Whitney   128
Euromissile   85
Explosive reactive armour   85

FADEC   63
Falkland Islands   10, 18, 22
Fenestron   31, 32
Fire suppression   107
Flat plate canopy   96, 97, 127
FLIR   129, 133, 134, 138
Fly-by-wire   60, 106, 139
French Army   82

G   100, 107, 131, 143
Global positioning system   124, 136
Grenade launcher   9, 12, 87, 126
Guns/cannon   9, 12, 73, 77, 78, 79, 80, 81, 102,
    104, 126, 127, 128, 129, 130, 131, 132, 133,
    135, 138, 140, 141, 142, 143
Gyroscope   59, 61, 63, 65, 66, 67, 70

Helicopters
  A–109, *Agusta* 137
  ABC, Sikorsky 117, 118, 119
  ACAP, Sikorsky S–75 114
  Alouette 2, Sud-Aviation 8, 9
  Apache, McDonnell Douglas AH–64 12, 13,
    79, 81, 84, 87, 90, 94, 97, 98, 105, 125, 126,
    127, 130, 131, 132, 133, 134, 135, 136, 137,
    138, 139, 144
  Black Hawk, Sikorsky UH–60 81, 97, 98,
    108
  Breguet-Richard Gyroplane No.1 2
  Bo–105, Messerschmitt-Bolkow-Blohm 88,
    90, 94
  Cheyenne, Lockheed AH–56 125, 126, 130
  Chinook, Boeing CH–47 17
  Cobra, Bell AH–1 9, 81, 85, 87, 94, 96, 97,
    125, 126, 127, 128, 129, 130, 131, 135, 136,
    137, 138, 139, 140, 144
  Commando, Westland 123
  Cornu 2, 3
  d'Ascanio 6
  EH–101, *Agusta*/Westland 21, 58, 99, 113
  FW–61, Focke-Wulf 6, 7
  Gazelle, Aérospatiale/Westland SA–341 14,
    15, 30, 32, 82, 87, 88, 90
  Halo, Mil Mi–26 19
  Havoc, Mil Mi–28 79, 80, 83, 87, 88, 94, 97,
    98, 105, 144
  Haze, Mil Mi–14 22
  Hind, Mil Mi–24/25/35 10, 12, 13, 14, 17,
    79, 81, 85, 87, 88, 90, 94, 103, 105, 106,
    125, 140, 141, 142, 143, 144
  Hip, Mil Mi–8 10, 17, 87, 103
  Hokum, Kamov 87
  Hook, Mil Mi–6 17, 44
  Hoplite, Mil Mi–2 87, 90
  Hound, Mil Mi–4 8
  Huey, Bell UH–1 8, 77, 126
  LHX 88, 118, 138
  Light attack helicopter 138, 140
  Lynx, Westland AH Mk 1/7 14, 16, 17, 18,
    21, 34, 35, 39, 62, 63, 70, 72, 77, 78, 88, 90,
    94, 99, 101, 113
  Mangusta, Agusta A–129 86, 87, 94, 125,
    127, 136, 137, 138, 139, 144
  MD 520N/530N, McDonnell Douglas 116
  NOTAR, McDonnell Douglas 98, 115, 116,
    117
  Oehmichen 3, 4
  OH–58, Bell 14, 89, 90, 94, 102, 119
  Osprey, Bell/Boeing V–22 119, 120
  PAH–2/HAC/HAP, Aérospatiale/MBB 88
  Pescara No. 3 3, 4
  Puma, Aérospatiale/Westland SA–330 17,
    21, 55, 72
  Rotodyne, Fairey 44
  R–4, Sikorsky 6, 8
  S–55, Sikorsky 6
  Sea Dragon, Sikorsky MH–53E 22
  Sea King, Sikorsky/Westland 20, 22, 23, 72
  Tiger, Aérospatiale/MBB 88, 90
  Tonal 88, 90, 140
  2 MG Omega, Bratukhin 6
  Whirlwind, Westland WS–55 8
  WG–30, Westland 55
  X–Wing, Sikorsky 114, 120
  XV–15, Bell 119
  YAH–63, Bell 130
  YAH–64, Hughes 130
Heli-Tele 14, 16
Helmet-mounted sight 79, 128, 133
Higher harmonic control 115
Honeywell 138
Hong Kong 88
Hughes 130
Hypervelocity missile 87

IFF 69
IHADSS 133, 134, 138
Inertial navigation system 70
Integrated multiplex system 139
International Standard Atmosphere 26, 131
IR
  Decoy flares 98, 101, 103, 143
  Jammer 98, 103, 104, 127, 144
  Paint 98, 127
  Signature 95, 98, 103, 127
  Smoke 104
  Suppression 57, 98, 99, 127, 144
Italian Army 137, 138, 139

Kamov 98
Kevlar 105, 112

Laser communications 123
Laser designator 14, 16, 82, 83, 90, 99, 101,
  128, 133, 134, 139, 142
Laser rangefinder 14, 81, 90, 99, 101, 128,
  133, 139
Laser warning receiver 101
Launoy 1
Lebanon 103
Lomonosov, Mikhail 1
Longbow 135
Limitations, helicopter 11

MAD 20
Mast-mounted sight 14, 85, 89, 90, 94, 139
Malaya 6
McDonnell Douglas 115, 130
Mil, Mikhail 140, 144
MIL. STD 1290 107
MIL. STD 1553 134, 139
Mine dispensers 87, 143
Mines 87
Missiles 8, 9, 12, 17, 18, 21, 77, 78, 81, 82, 83,
  85, 87, 93, 95, 98, 101, 102, 103, 104, 125,
  126, 127, 129, 131, 140, 141, 144
  AC3G 85

Blowpipe 143
Exocet 21
FITOW 84, 85
Harpoon 21
Hellfire 13, 82, 83, 84, 90, 128, 129, 130,
    131, 134, 135, 138, 139
HOT 82, 85, 88, 90, 138
Milan 18
Mistral 133, 138
PARS–3 85
SA–7 87, 90
Sea Eagle 21
Sea Skua 21
Sidearm 133
Sidewinder 13, 87, 129, 132, 138
Spiral 83, 90, 141, 143
Starstreak 133
Stinger 12, 13, 86, 90, 98, 129, 133, 136,
    138, 143
Swatter 141
Swingfire 85
TOW 77, 78, 82, 84, 85, 90, 127, 128, 129,
    131, 137, 138, 139
TRIGAT 85, 90
Missile approach warner 102
Multi-function display 74, 75

Nap of the earth 41, 134
NATO 10, 12, 14, 17, 94, 100, 107, 132, 140,
    141, 142
Newton, Sir Isaac 2
Northern Ireland 88
Night vision equipment 128, 129, 141, 142

Otto, N.A. 2

Pescara, Marquis de 3, 4
Phillips, Horatio 2
PNVS 90, 133, 134, 138
Polish Air Force 87
Ponton d'Amecourt, Visconte de 2

Racal 70, 71
Radar 20, 21, 22, 71, 72, 73, 90, 94, 98, 99,
    100, 101, 102, 103, 104, 114, 127, 129, 134,
    136, 139
    Longbow 133
    Orchidée 72
    Searchwater 22, 72, 73
    Sea Searcher 72
    Sea Spray 21, 72

Radar jammer 103, 127
Radar signature 95, 98, 114, 127, 129
Radar warning receiver 100, 101, 103, 127
Reconnaissance/surveillance 6, 14, 15, 17, 71,
    88, 99, 108, 115, 143
Ring laser gyro 59, 70
RNS 252 70, 71
Rockets 9, 12, 13, 73, 77, 78, 81, 84, 85, 126,
    127, 129, 130, 131, 132, 138, 141, 142, 143
Rolls-Royce 52, 53, 54, 58
Royal Air Force 5, 6, 69
Royal Marines 69
Royal Navy 5, 22, 69, 123

SAR 23, 62, 69
Side arm controls 121
Sikorsky Helicopters 114, 117, 120
Sikorsky, Igor 6
Sonar 20
Sonobuoy 20
Stability augmentation 38, 60, 61, 131
Surface-to-air missiles 12, 86, 143

TADS 90, 132, 133, 134, 135, 138
TANS 70
Thermal imaging 14, 15, 71, 73, 90, 99
Tilt rotor 119
Torpedo 20
Turbomeca 51, 52, 55, 58

US Air Force 120
US Army 125, 129, 130, 131
US Marine Corps 120, 128, 129
US Navy 120

Vibration 77, 79, 87, 103, 114, 115, 122, 129,
    133
Vietnam 8, 9, 10, 11, 18, 77, 87, 125, 126, 140
Visual signature 95

Warsaw Pact 10, 12, 14, 17, 100, 107, 140,
    142
Westland Helicopters 55, 110, 112
Wire cutters 102
Wright brothers 2, 111

Yugoslav Air Force 87
Yuriev, Boris 3